THE TARANTINO COLLECTION

WWW.MUSICSALES.COM

THE TARANTINO COLLECTION PUBLISHED BY: WISE PUBLICATIONS 8/9 FRITH STREET, LONDON W1D 3JB, ENGLAND

EXCLUSIVE DISTRIBUTORS: MUSIC SALES LIMITED DISTRIBUTION CENTRE, NEWMARKET ROAD, BURY ST. EDMUNDS, SUFFOLK IP33 3YB, ENGLAND

MUSIC SALES PTY LIMITED 120 ROTHSCHILD AVENUE, ROSEBERY, NSW 2018, AUSTRALIA

ORDER NO: AM980837 • ISBN: 1-84449-665-1 • THIS BOOK © COPYRIGHT 2004 BY WISE PUBLICATIONS

COMPILED BY NICK CRISPIN • MUSIC EDITED BY TOM FLEMING • MUSIC ARRANGED BY MARTIN SHELLARD

MUSIC PROCESSED BY PAUL EWERS MUSIC DESIGN • COVER DESIGN BY FRESH LEMON

PHOTOGRAPHS COURTESY OF LONDON FEATURES INTERNATIONAL & REX FEATURES

PRINTED IN THE UNITED KINGDOM BY PRINTWISE (HAVERHILL) LIMITED HAVERHILL, SUFFOLK

WISE PUBLICATIONS / PART OF THE MUSIC SALES GROUP LONDON / NEW YORK / PARIS / SYDNEY / COPENHAGEN / BERLIN / MADRID / TOKYO

BANG BANG (MY BABY SHOT ME DOWN)

Words & Music by Sonny Bono

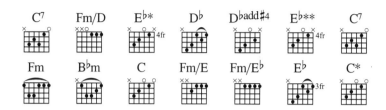

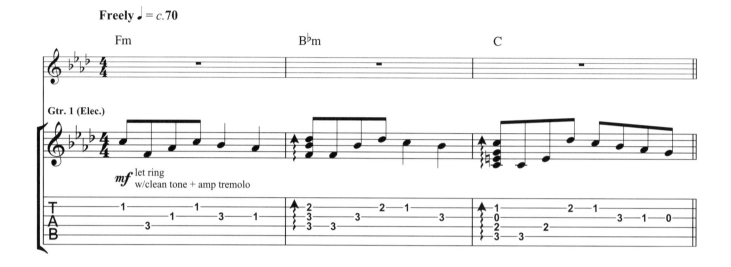

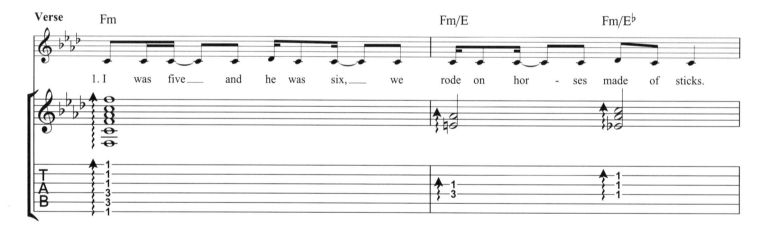

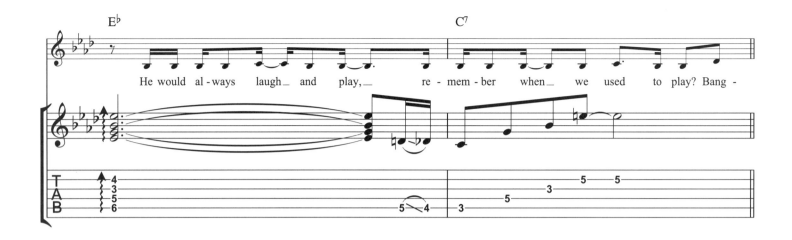

He would al-ways laugh_ and play,_ re-mem-ber when_ we used to play? Bang-

Chorus Fm

-bang, I shot you down. Bang-bang,_ you hit the ground._ Bang-

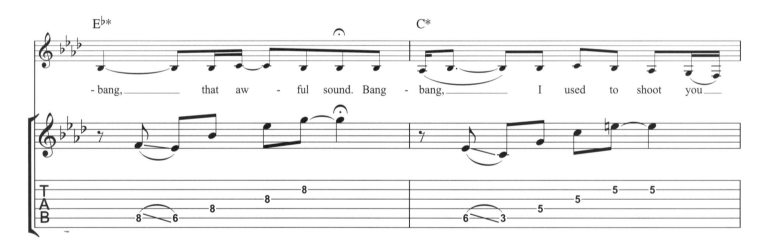

-bang,_____ that aw - ful sound. Bang-bang,_____ I used to shoot you_

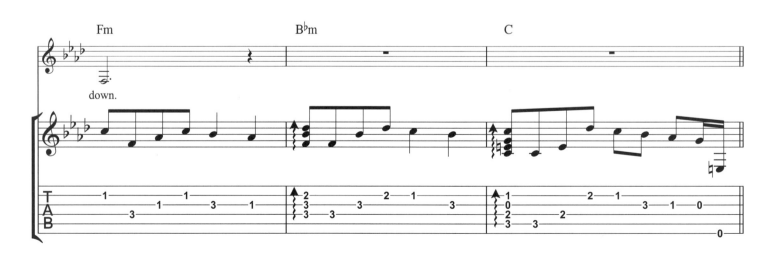

down.

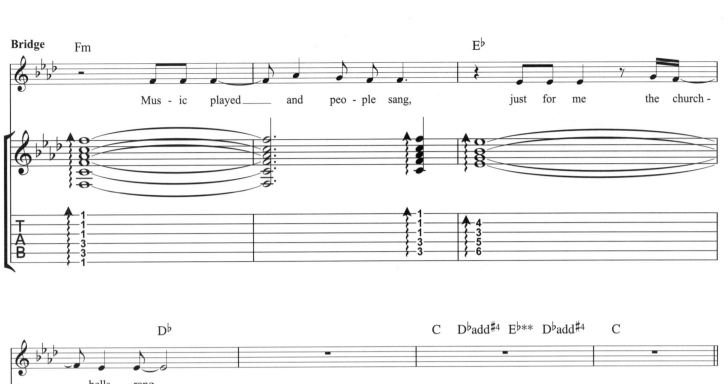

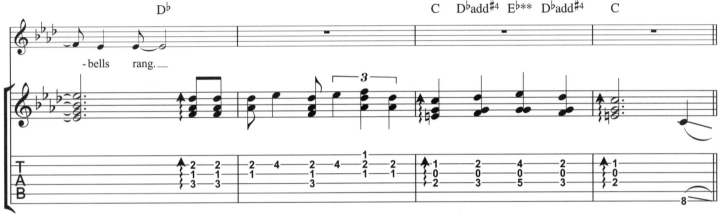

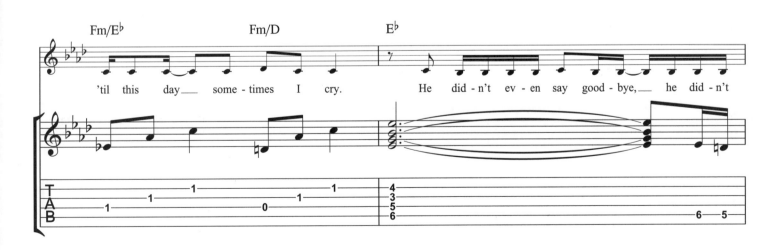

BATTLE WITHOUT HONOR OR HUMANITY

By Tomoyasu Hotei

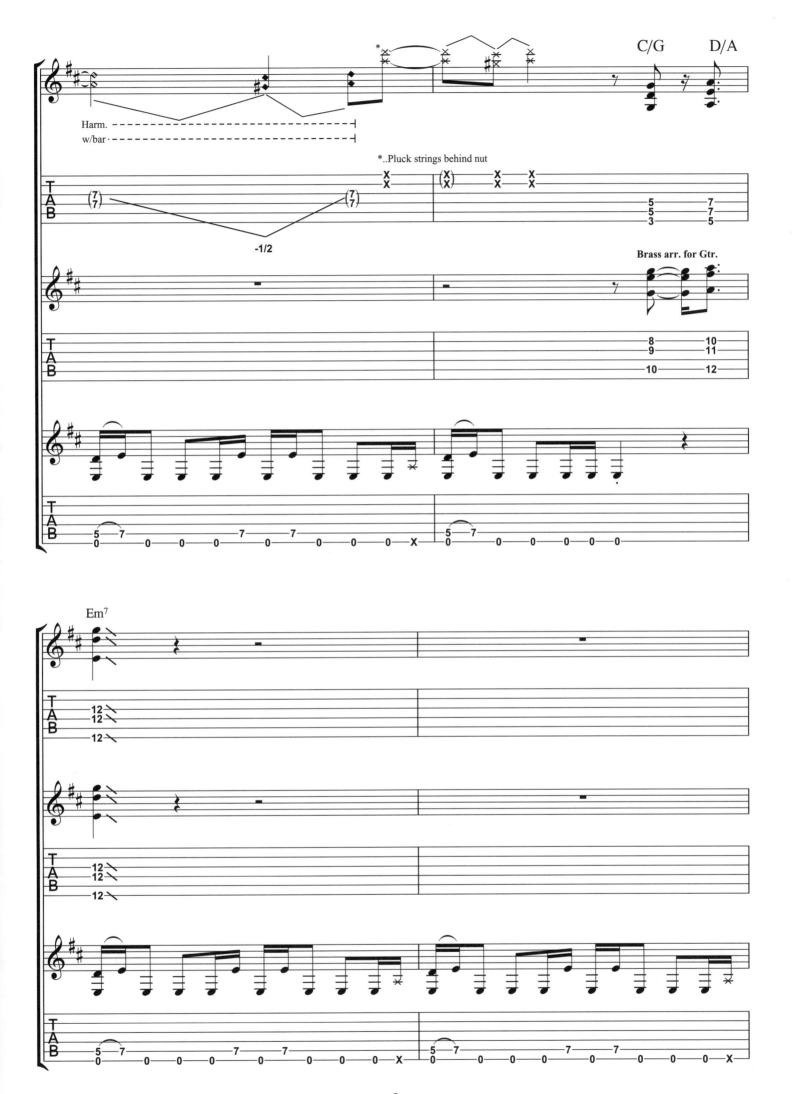

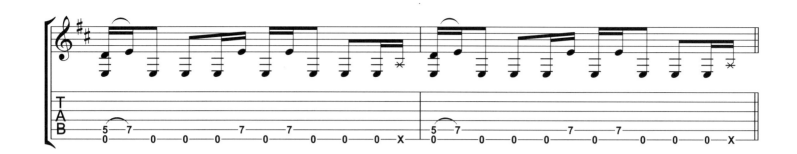

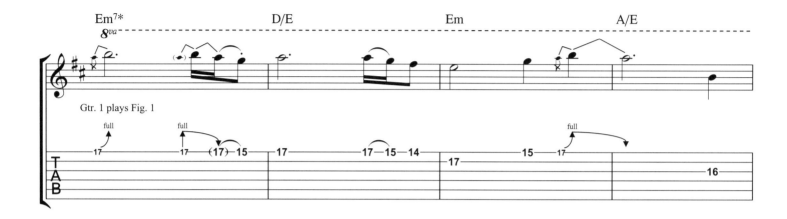

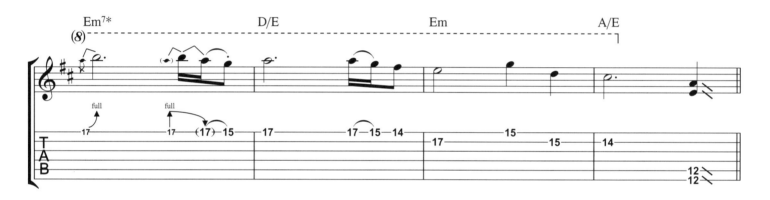

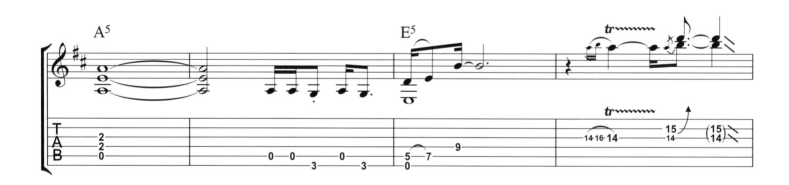

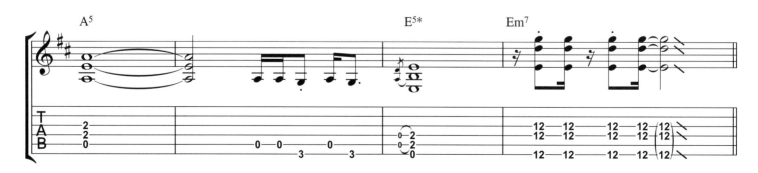

10

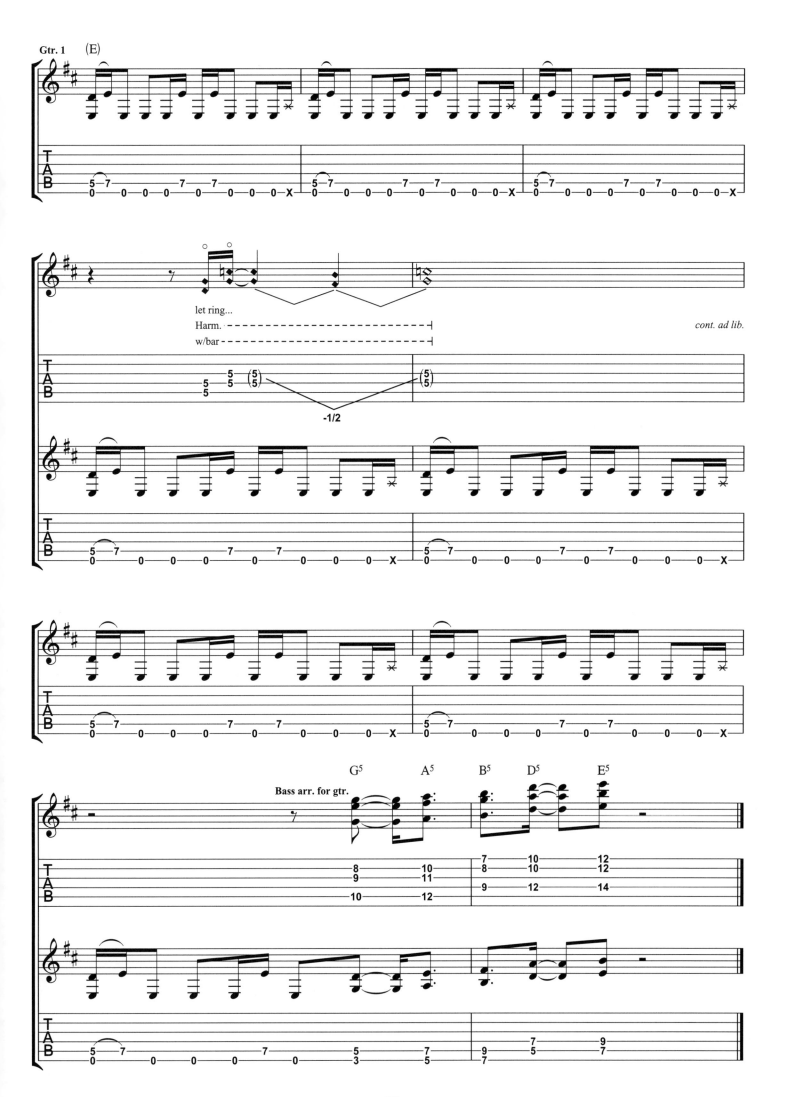

BUSTIN' SURFBOARDS

By Gerald Sanders, Jesse Sanders,
Norman Sanders & Leonard Delaney

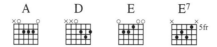

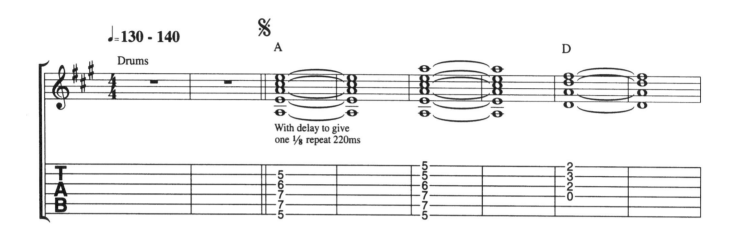

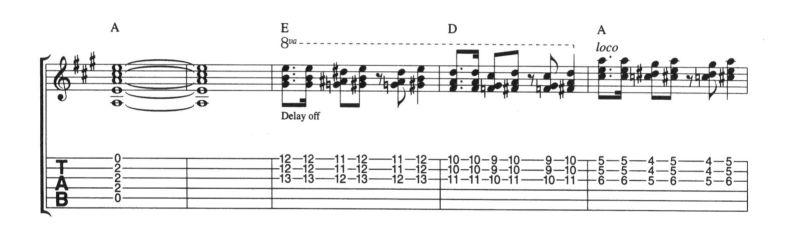

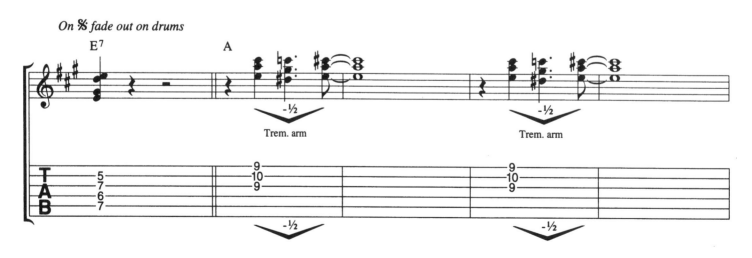

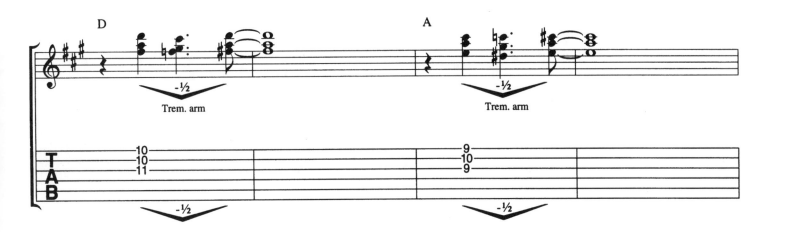

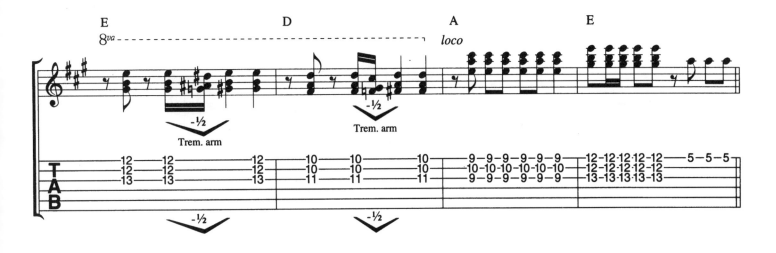

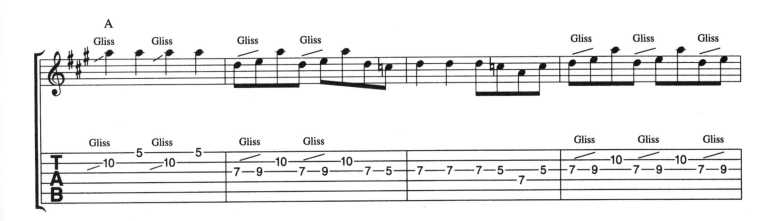

13

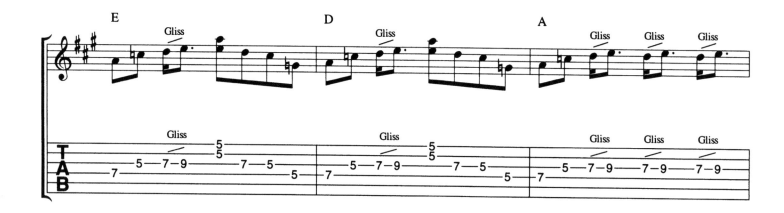

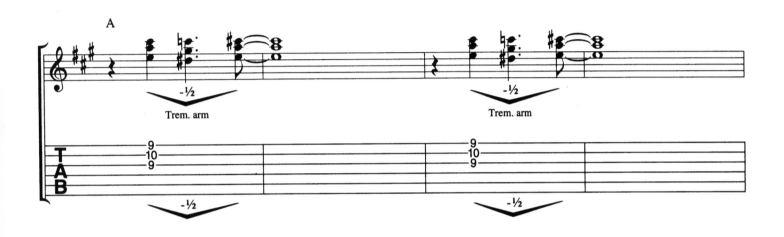

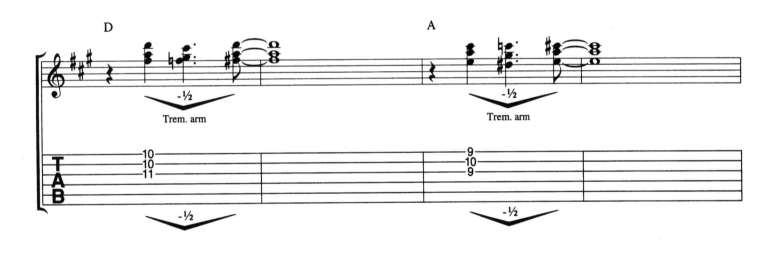

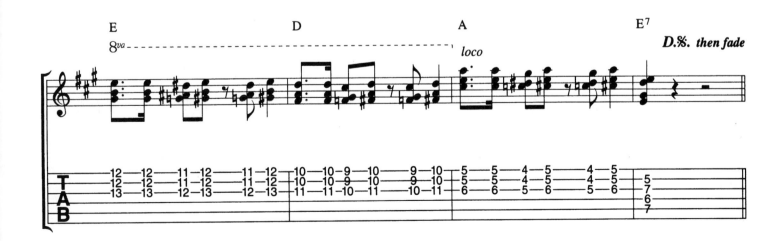

GIRL, YOU'LL BE A WOMAN SOON

Words & Music by Neil Diamond

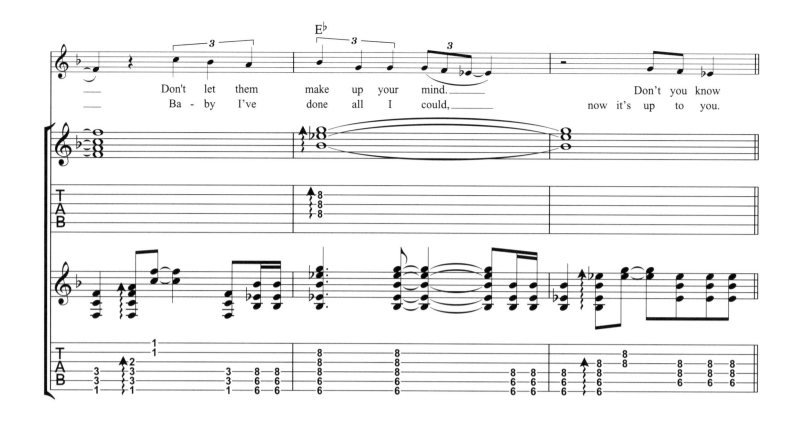

Don't let them make up your mind.   Don't you know
Ba - by I've done all I could,   now it's up to you.

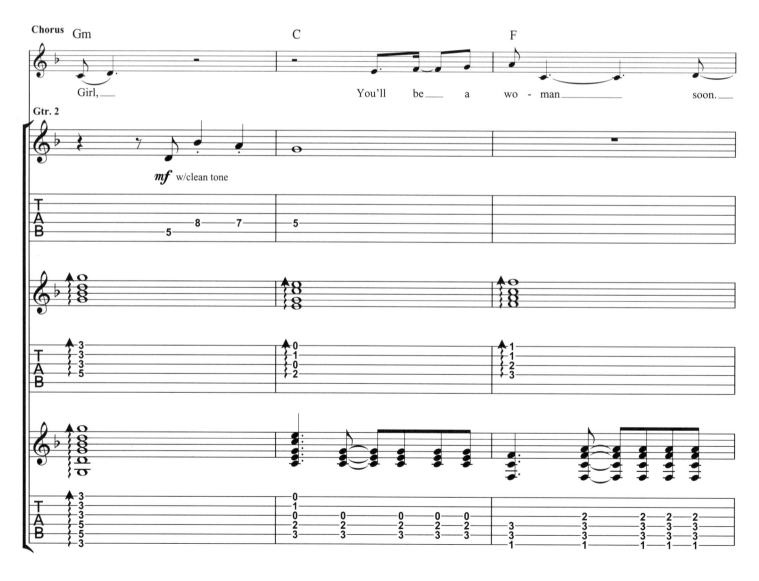

Chorus

Girl,   You'll be a wo - man   soon.

mf w/clean tone

Gtr. 2

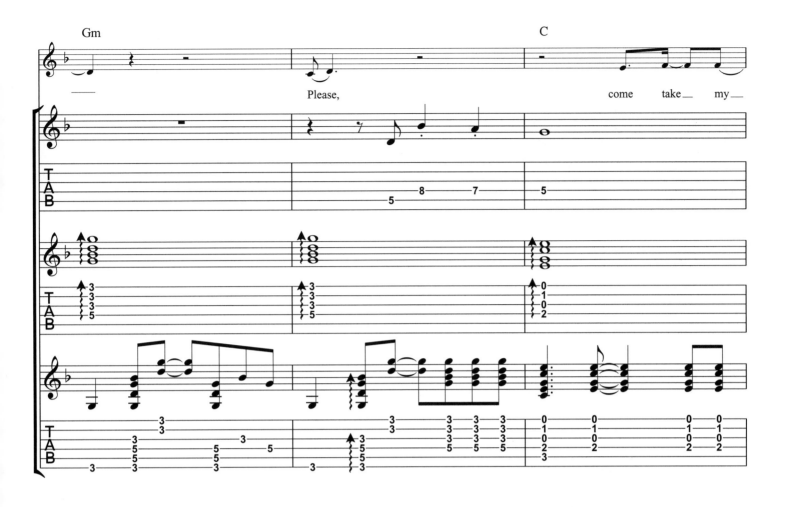

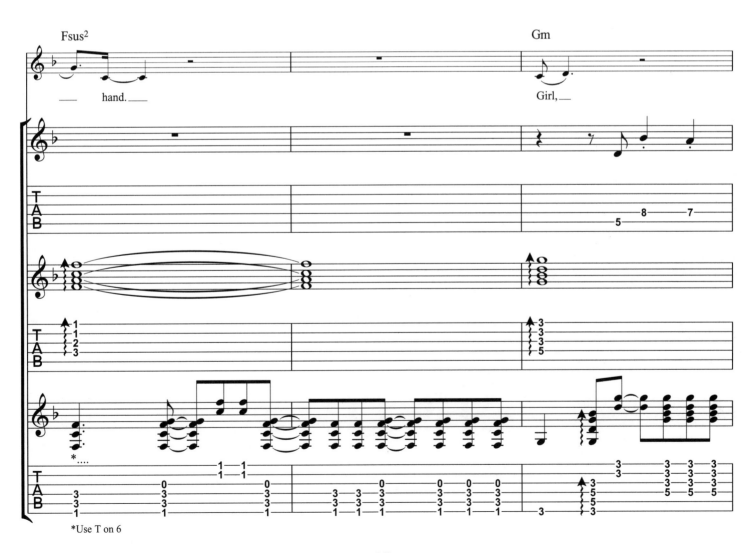

*Use T on 6

19

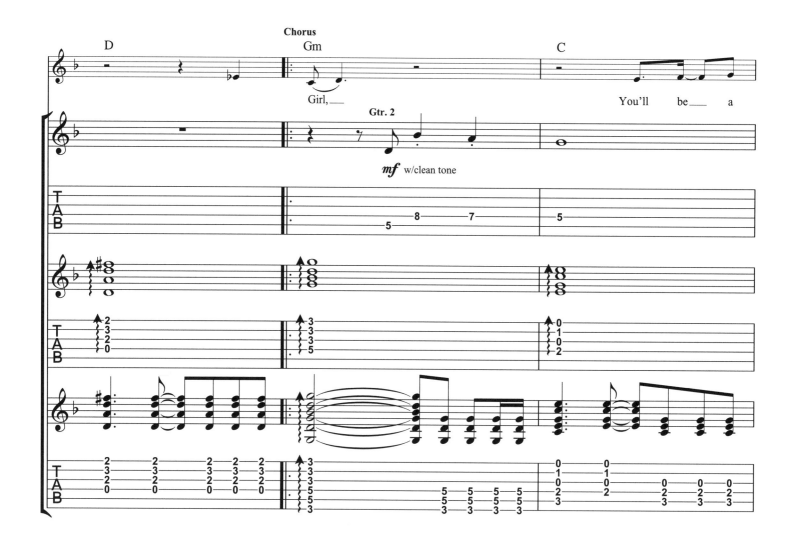

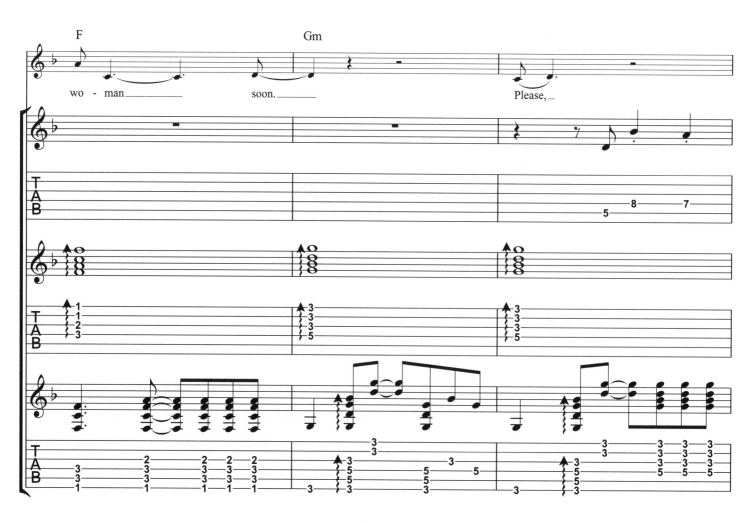

*Use T on 6

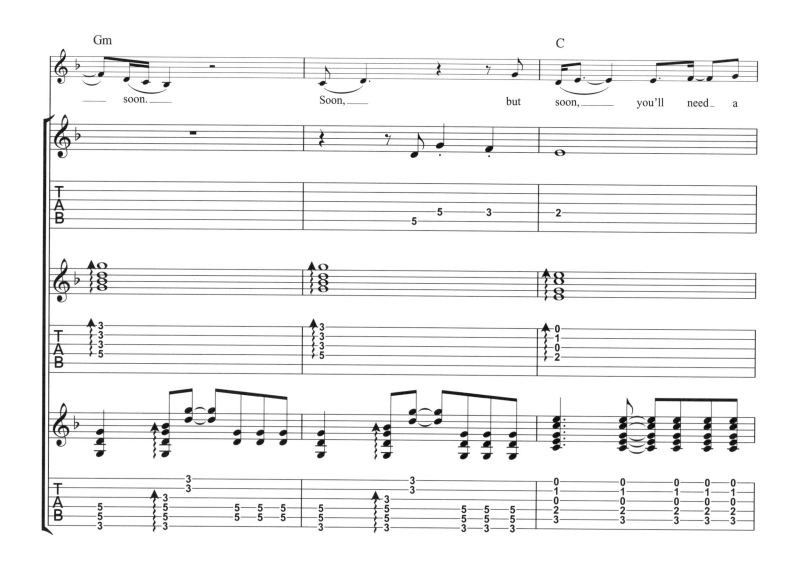

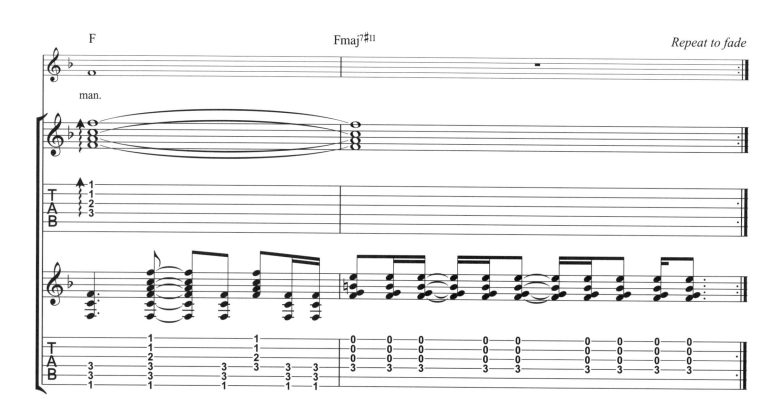

GOODNIGHT MOON

Words & Music by Ambrosia Parsley & Duke McVinnie

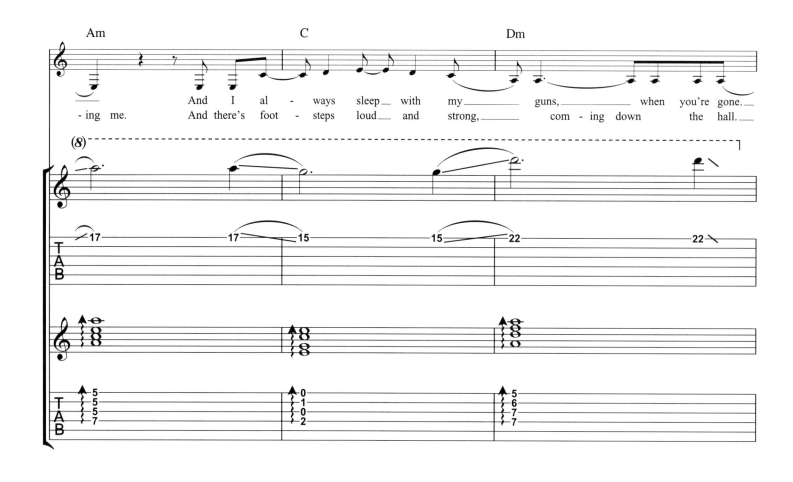

And I al - ways sleep_ with my_____ guns,_____ when you're gone.

- ing me. And there's foot - steps loud and strong,_____ com - ing down the hall.

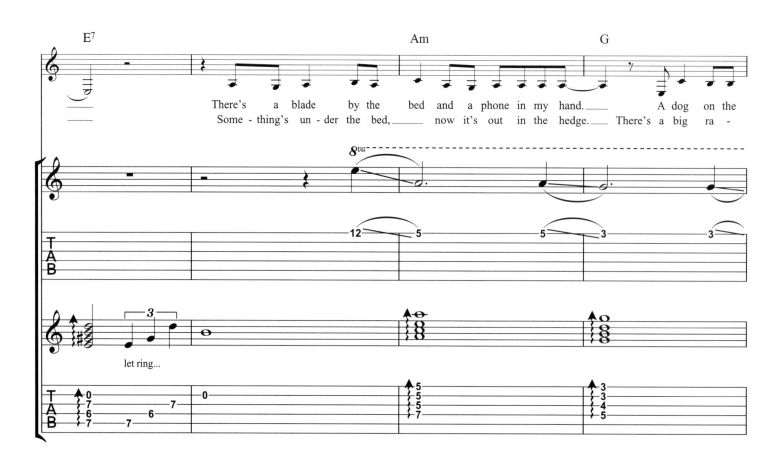

There's a blade by the bed and a phone in my hand.___ A dog on the

Some - thing's un - der the bed,_____ now it's out in the hedge.___ There's a big ra -

let ring...

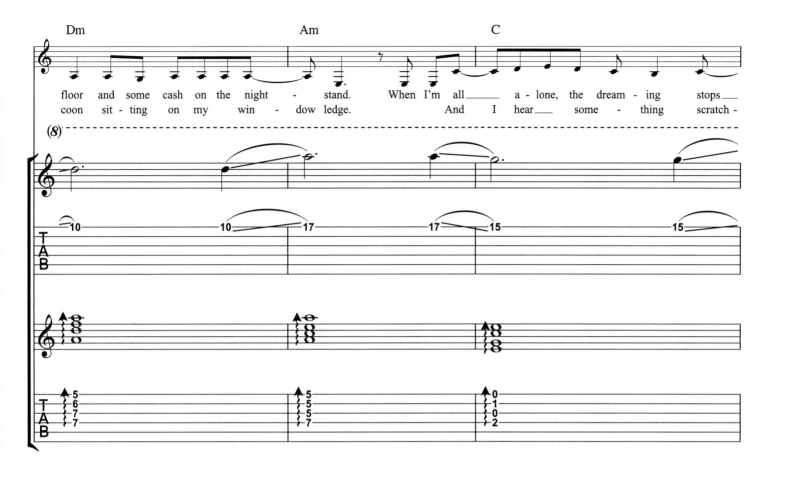

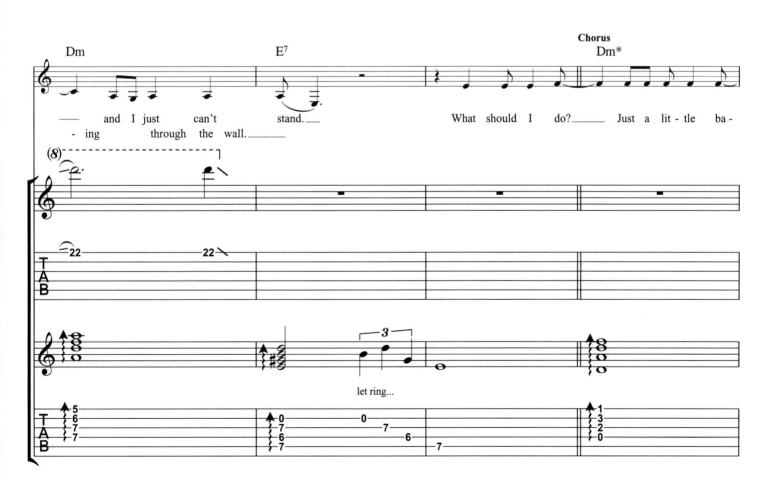

28

2. There's a shark in the

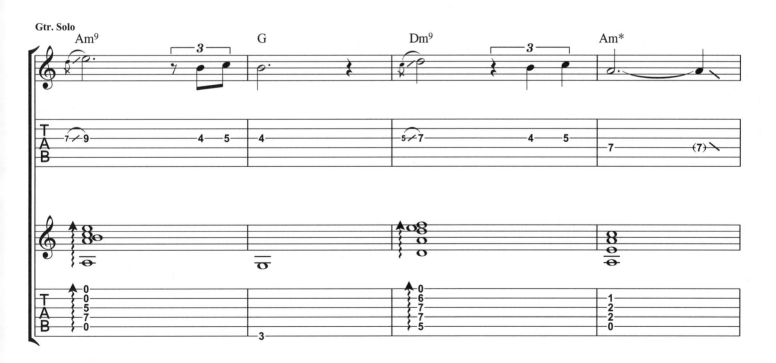

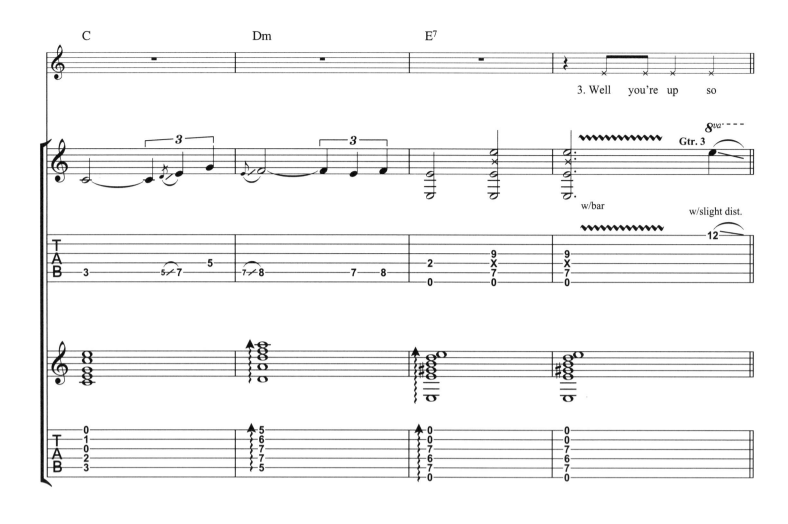

3. Well you're up so

w/bar   w/slight dist.

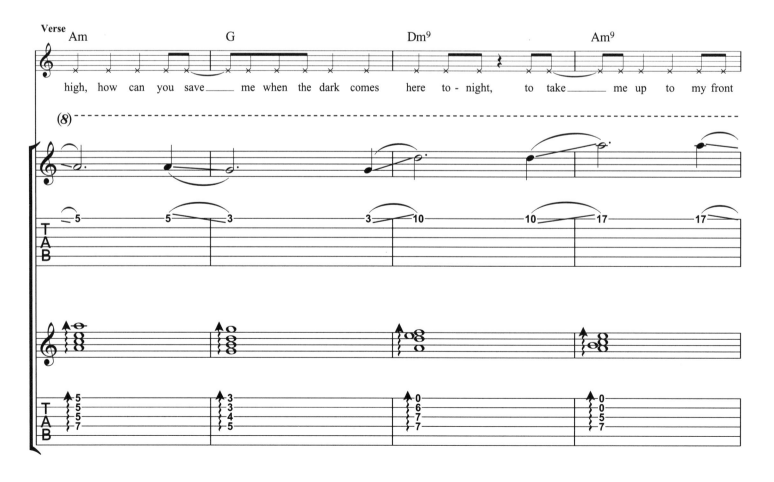

high, how can you save ___ me when the dark comes here to - night, to take ___ me up to my front

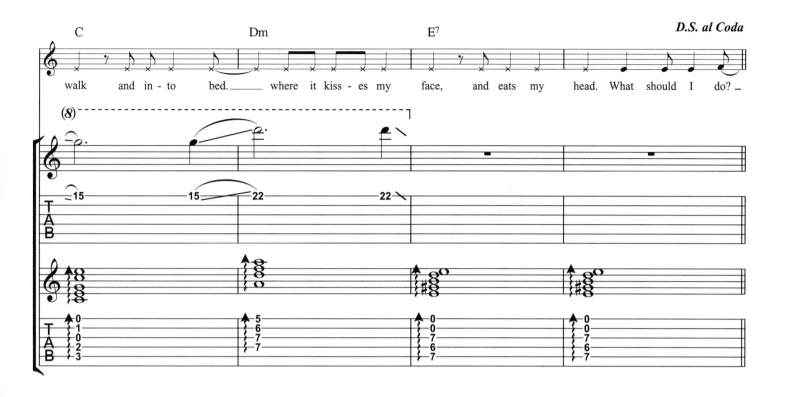

walk and in-to bed.___ where it kiss-es my face, and eats my head. What should I do?___

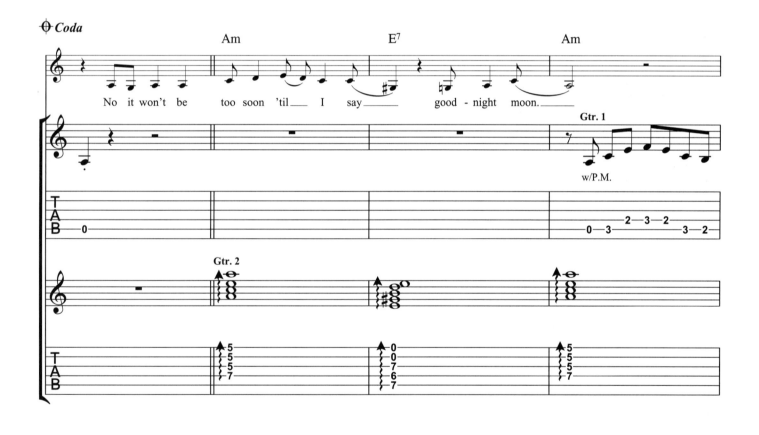

⊕ *Coda*

No it won't be too soon 'til___ I say_____ good-night moon.___

Gtr. 1

w/P.M.

Gtr. 2

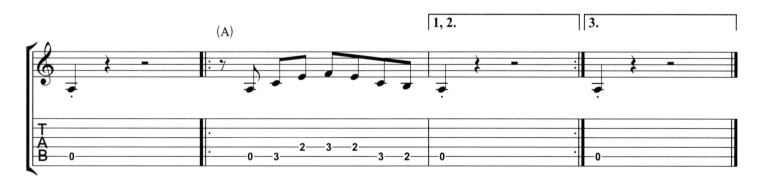

(A)

1, 2.   3.

JUNGLE BOOGIE

Words & Music by Ronald Bell, Robert Bell, Claydes Smith, George Brown, Dennis Thomas, Robert Mickens, Donald Boyce & Richard Westfield

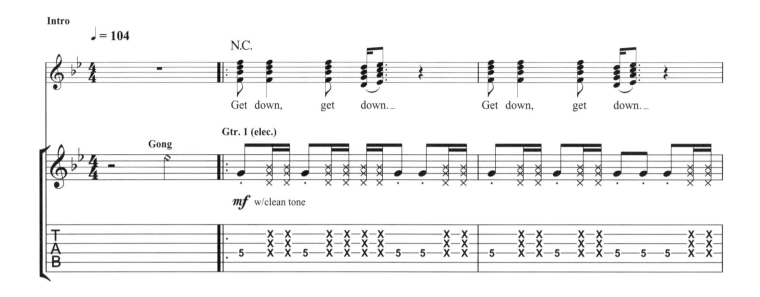

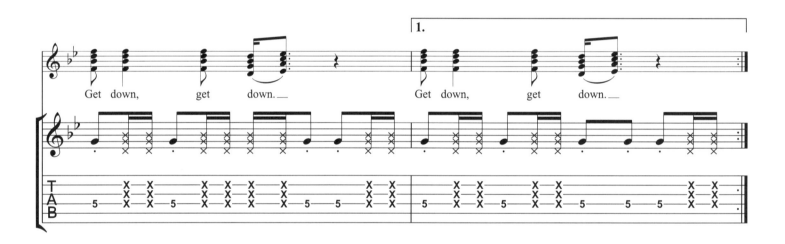

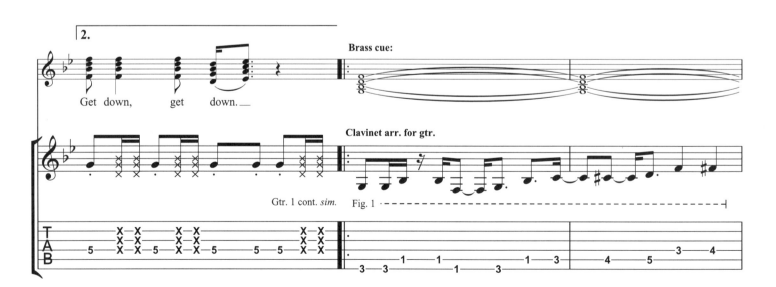

Fig. 2

2° w/Fig. 2

2° w/Fig. 1

*Spoken: Get down wi' da boogie,   get it on.   Get down wi' da boogie,

(Jun - gle   boo - gie.)   (Jun - gle   boo - gie.)   (Jun - gle   boo - gie.)

Gtr. 1

*2° spoken part ad lib. *sim.*

get it on.   Get up wi' da boogie,   get up wi' da get down.

(Jun - gle   boo - gie.)   (Jun - gle   boo - gie.)   (Jun - gle   boo - gie.)

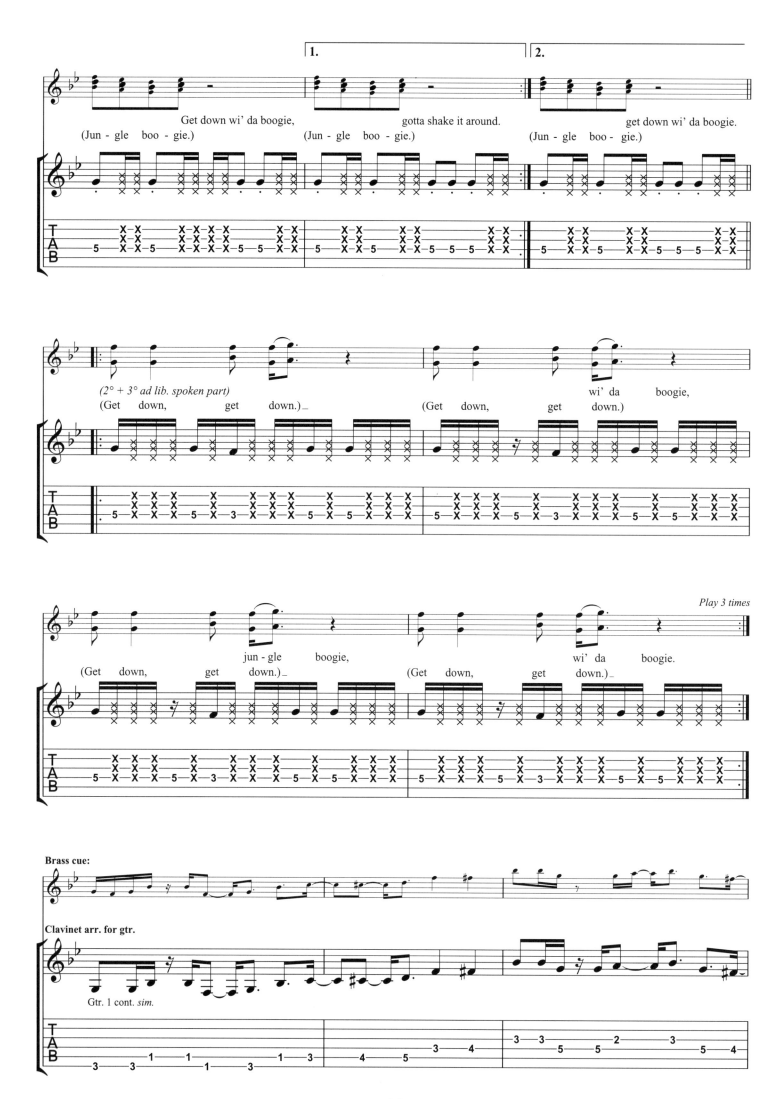

34

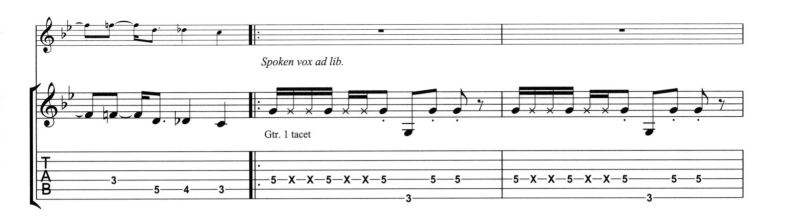

Spoken vox ad lib.

Gtr. 1 tacet

Play 5 times

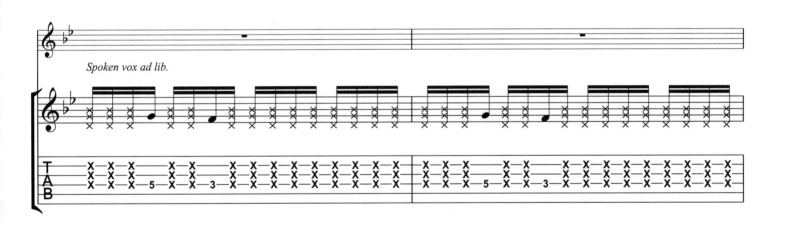

Spoken vox ad lib.

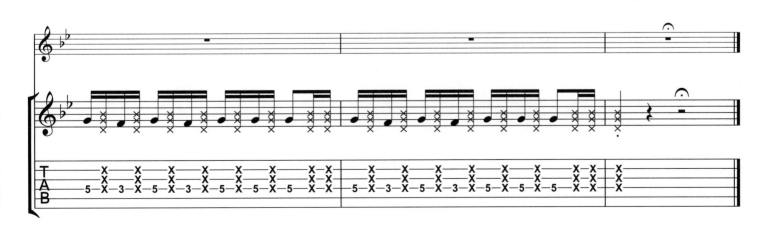

35

LITTLE GREEN BAG

Words & Music by Jan Visser & James Bouwens

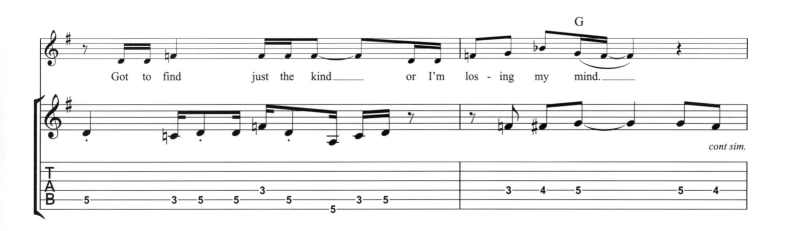

Got to find just the kind___ or I'm los-ing my mind.___

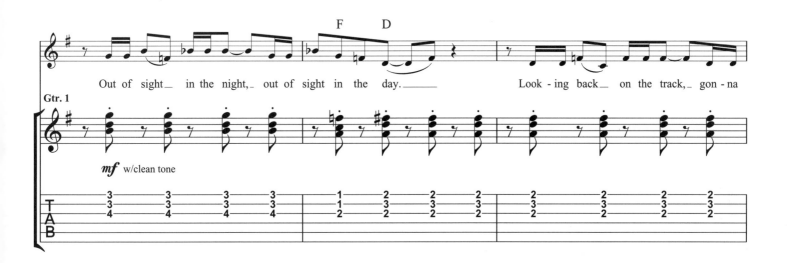

Out of sight___ in the night,___ out of sight in the day.___ Look-ing back___ on the track,_ gon-na

do it my way.___ Out of sight___ in the night,___ out of sight in the day.___

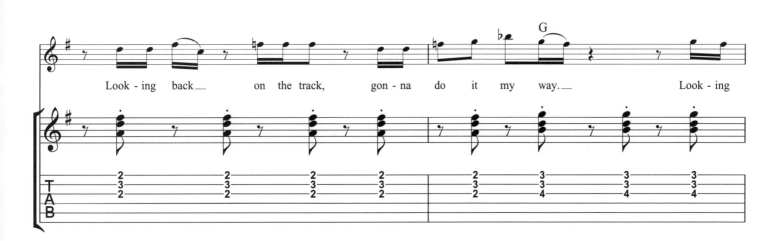

Look-ing back___ on the track, gon-na do it my way.___ Look-ing

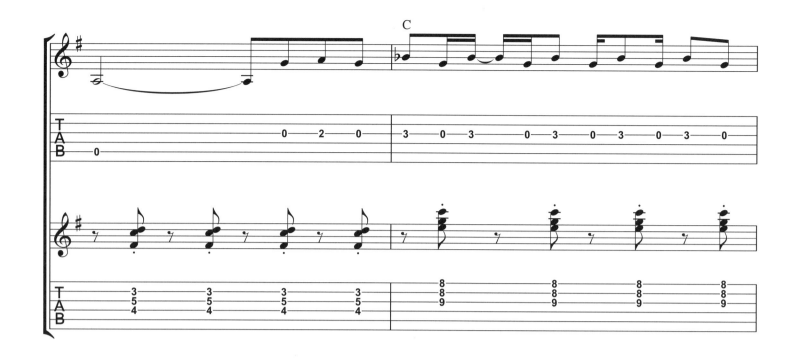

Chorus G

Look - ing for some hap - pi - ness__ but there__ is on - ly lone - li - ness__ to find.

Gtr. 3 tacet

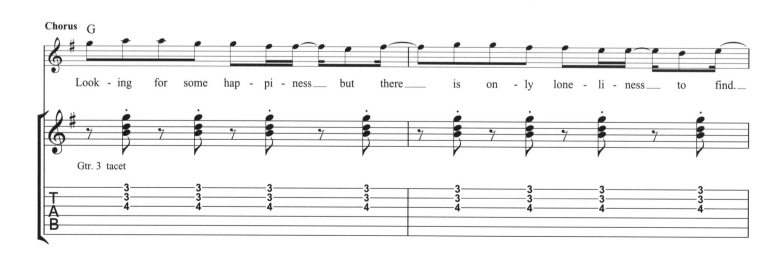

Jump__ to the

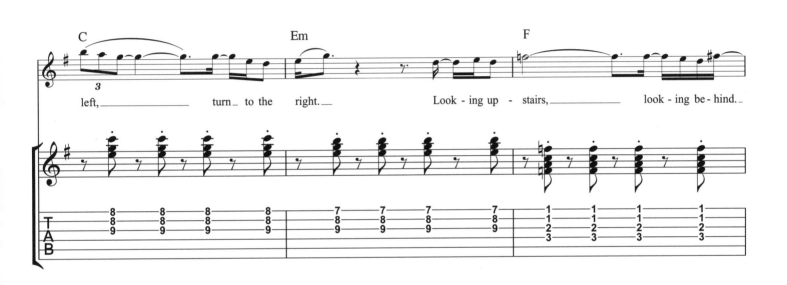

left,_____ turn__ to the right.__ Look - ing up - stairs,_____ look - ing be - hind.__

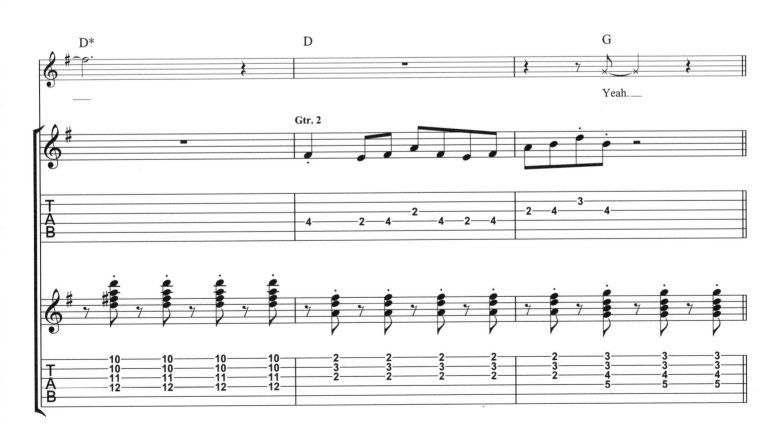

Yeah.__

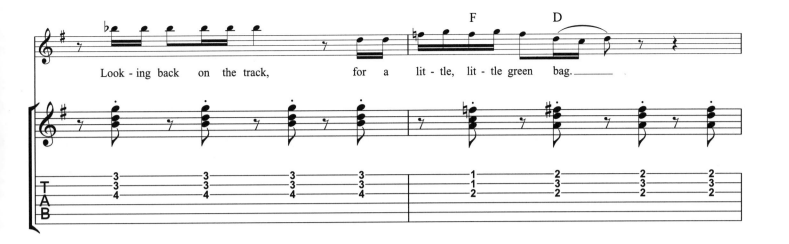

Look-ing back on the track, for a lit-tle, lit-tle green bag.____

Got to find just the kind, or I'm los-ing my mind.____

Interlude
Gtr. 3

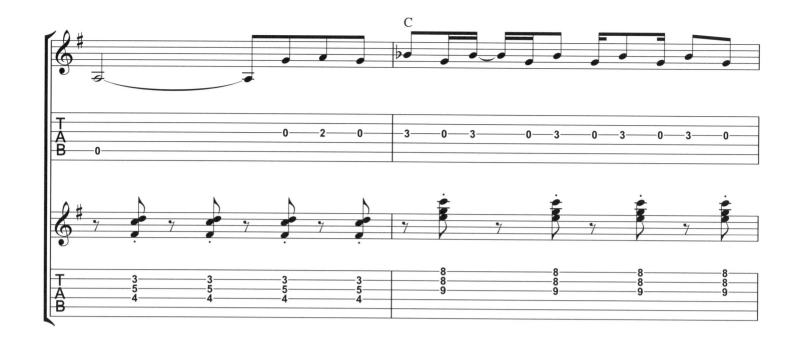

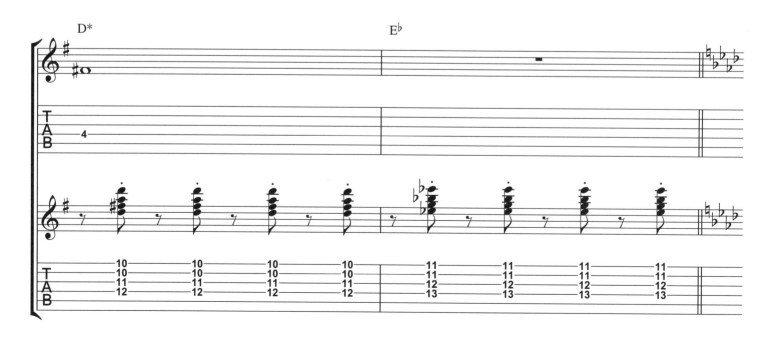

Ba, ba, ba, ba, ba.___ Ba, ba, ba, ba, ba, ba, ba, ba, ba.___ Ba, ba, ba, ba,

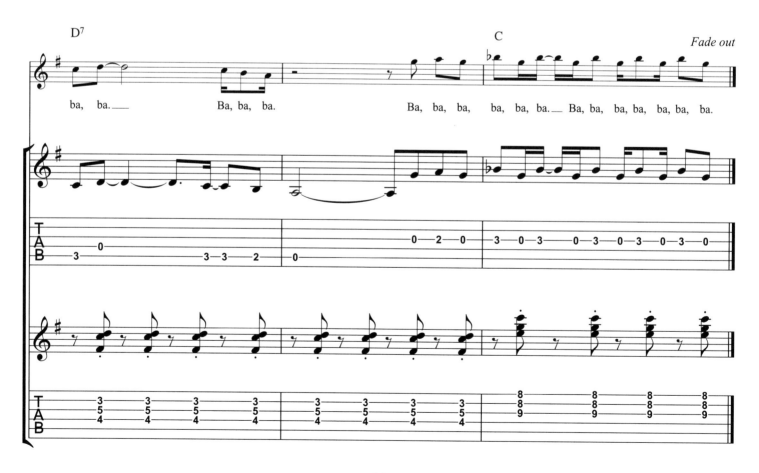

ba, ba.___ Ba, ba, ba. Ba, ba, ba, ba, ba, ba.___ Ba, ba, ba, ba, ba, ba, ba.

MISIRLOU

By Nicholas Roubanis

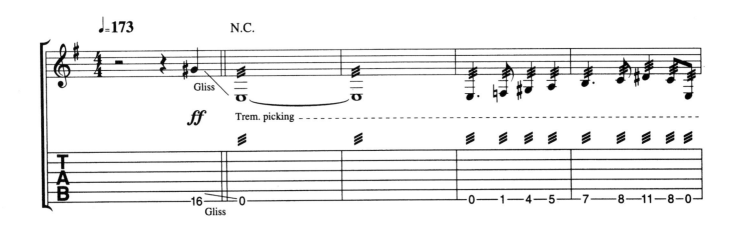

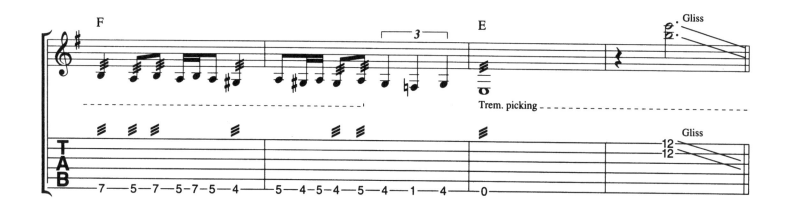

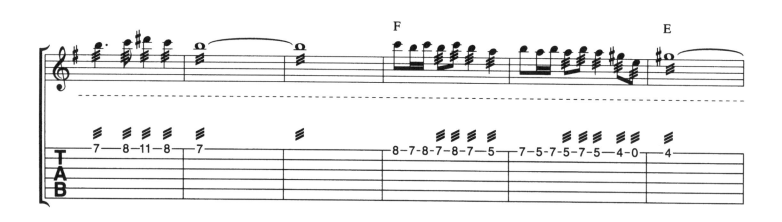

48

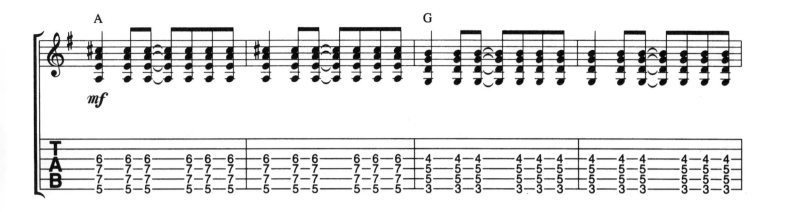

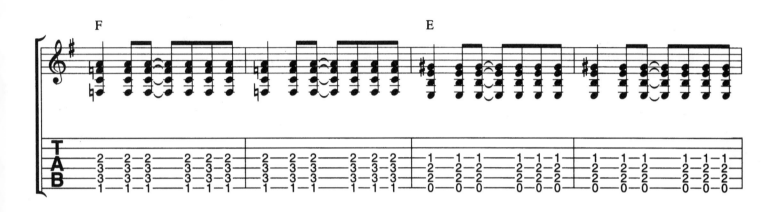

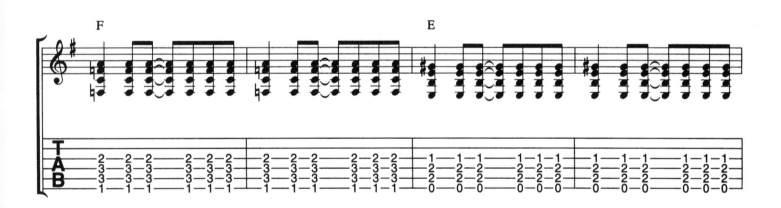

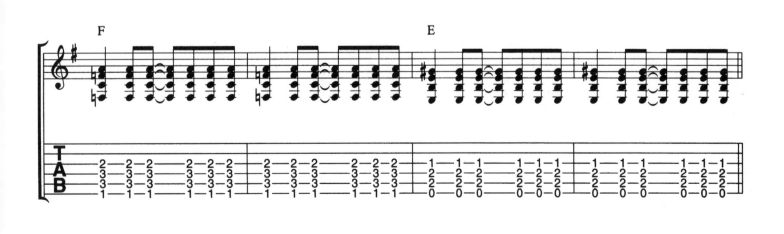

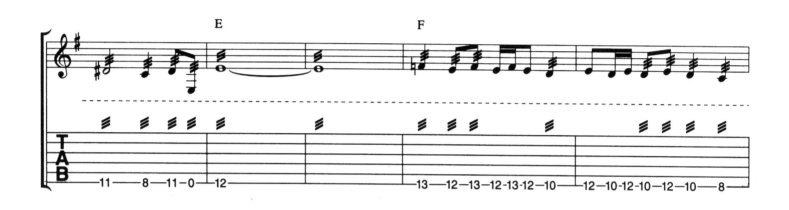

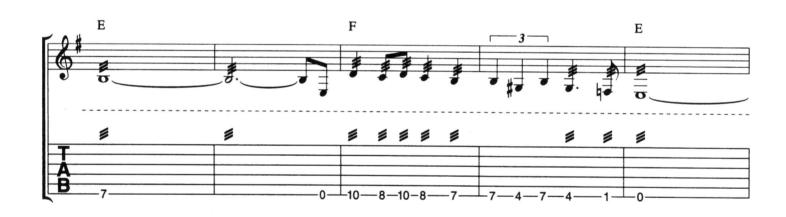

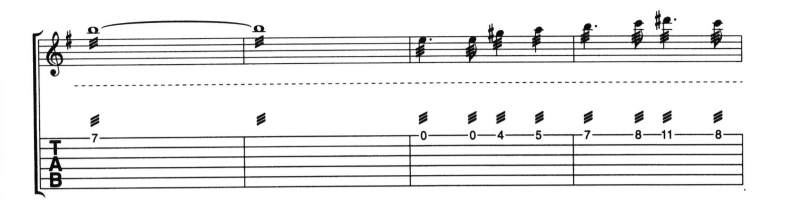

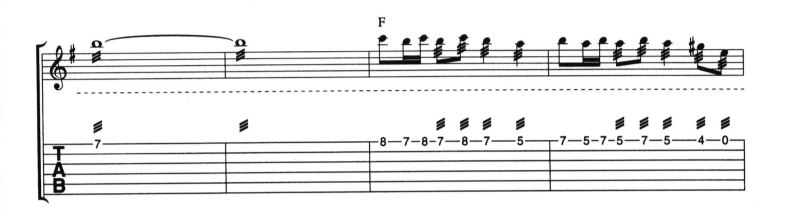

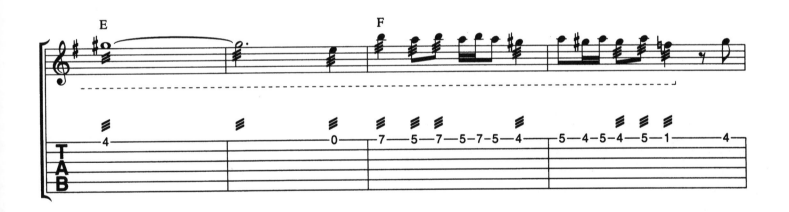

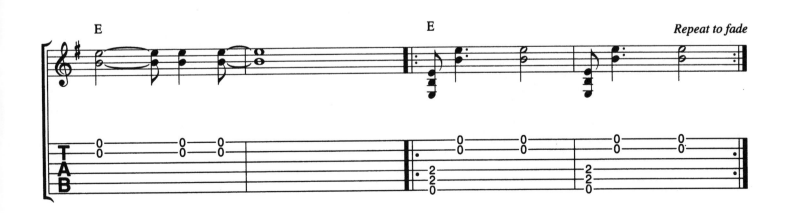

RUMBLE

By Link Wray & Milton Grant

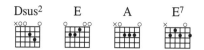

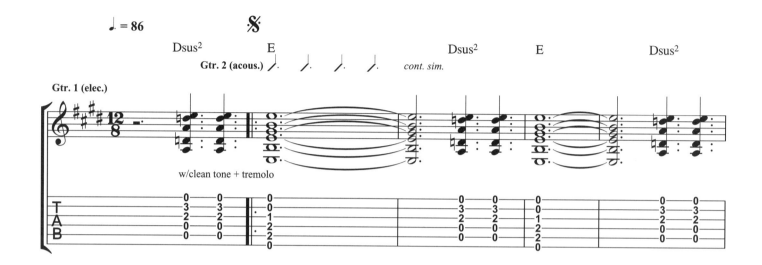

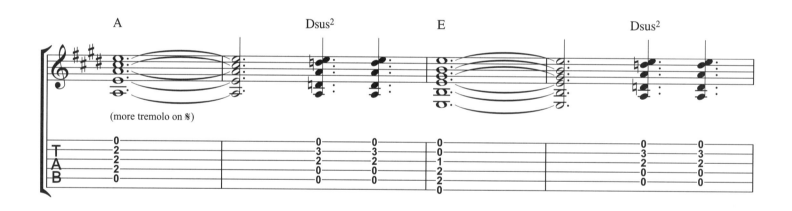

SCOOBY SNACKS

Words & Music by Huey Morgan, Brian Leiser, Steve Borgovini, Daniel Ash, Kevin Haskins, Glenn Campling & Quentin Tarantino

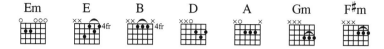

Tune down 1 tone and slightly flat

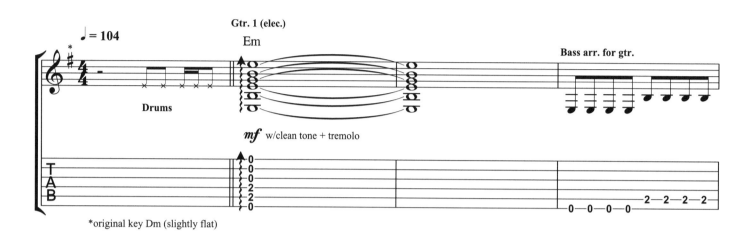

*original key Dm (slightly flat)

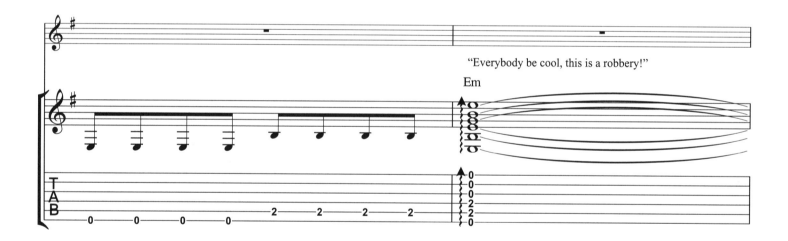

"Everybody be cool, this is a robbery!"

"Any of you fucking pricks move, and I'll execute every motherfucking last one of you!"

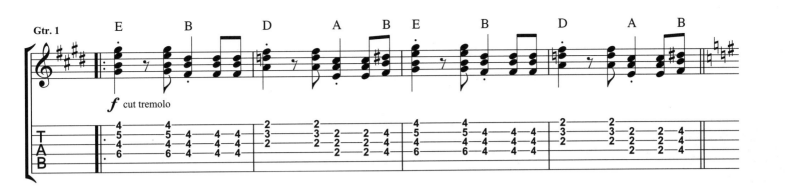

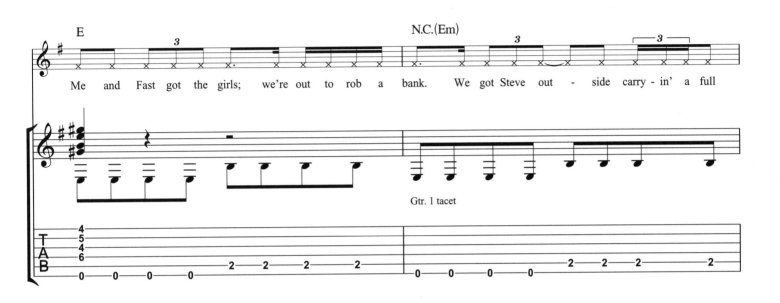

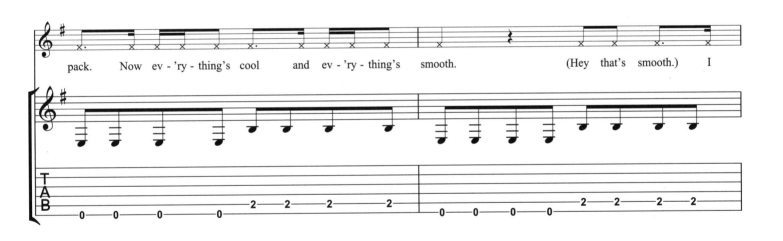

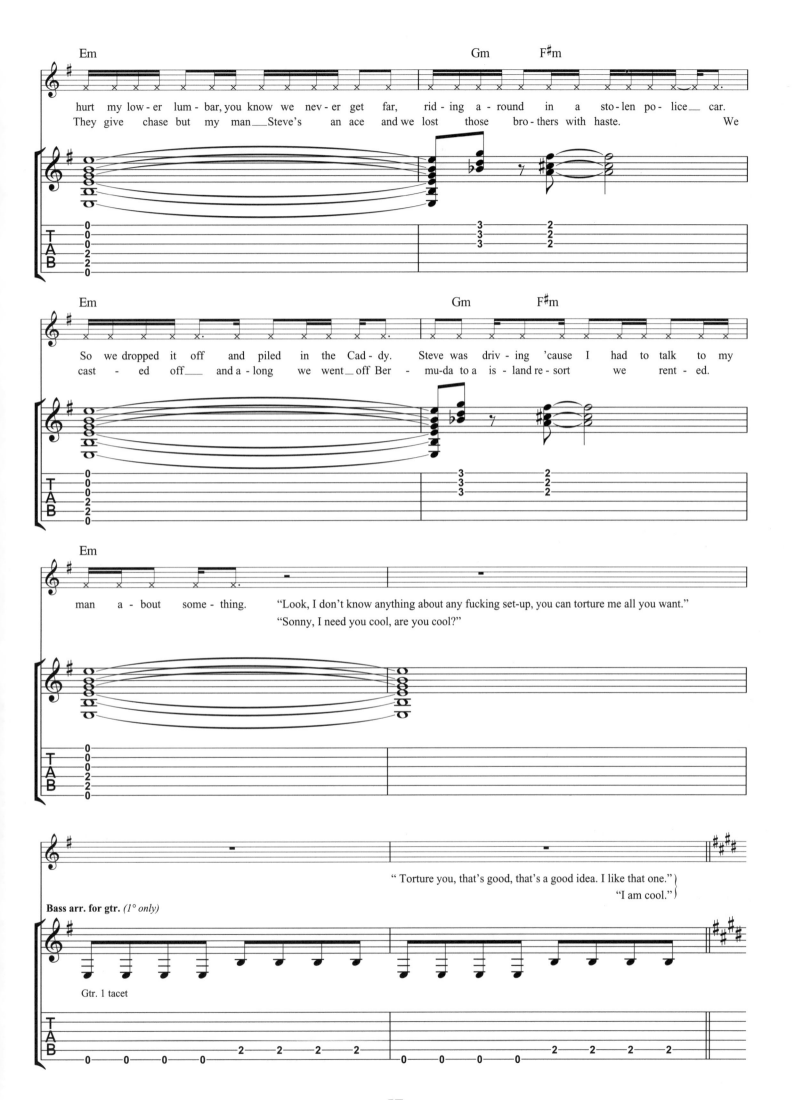

hurt my low-er lum-bar, you know we nev-er get far, rid-ing a-round in a sto-len po-lice car.
They give chase but my man Steve's an ace and we lost those bro-thers with haste. We

So we dropped it off and piled in the Cad-dy. Steve was driv-ing 'cause I had to talk to my
cast-ed off and a-long we went off Ber-mu-da to a is-land re-sort we rent-ed.

man a-bout some-thing. "Look, I don't know anything about any fucking set-up, you can torture me all you want."
"Sonny, I need you cool, are you cool?"

" Torture you, that's good, that's a good idea. I like that one."
"I am cool."

Bass arr. for gtr. *(1° only)*

Gtr. 1 tacet

SON OF A PREACHER MAN

Words & Music by John Hurley & Ronnie Wilkins

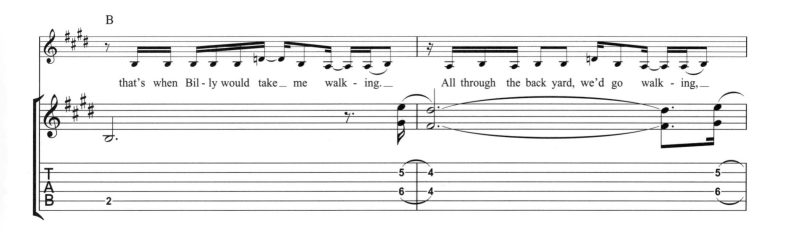

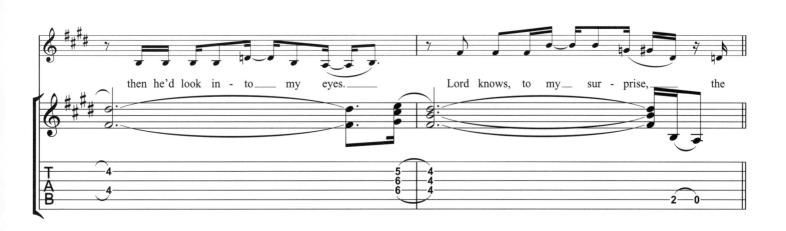

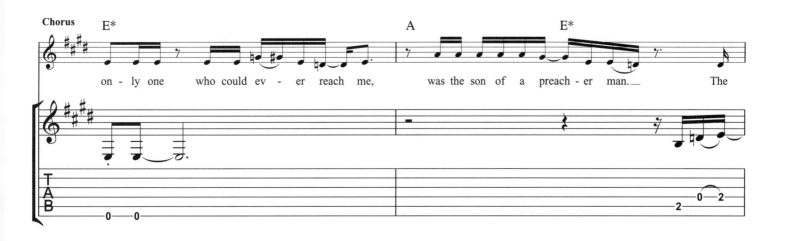

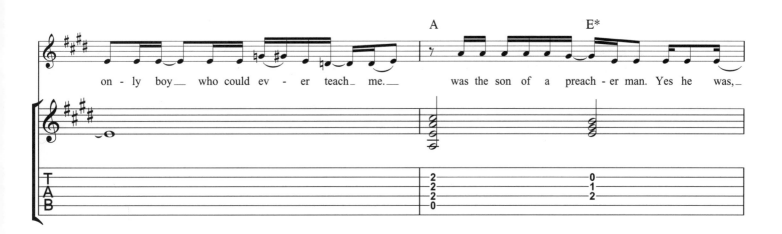

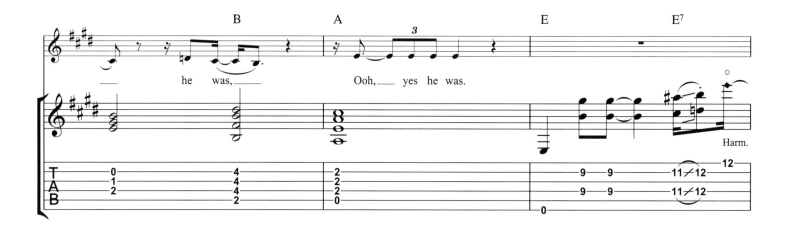

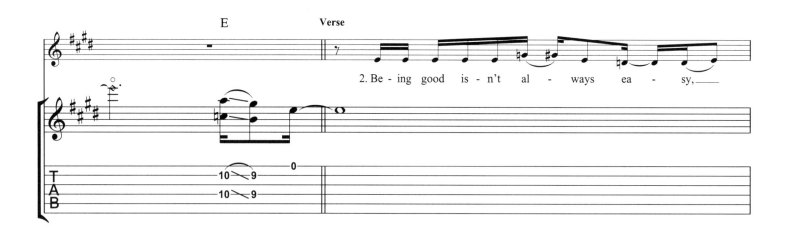

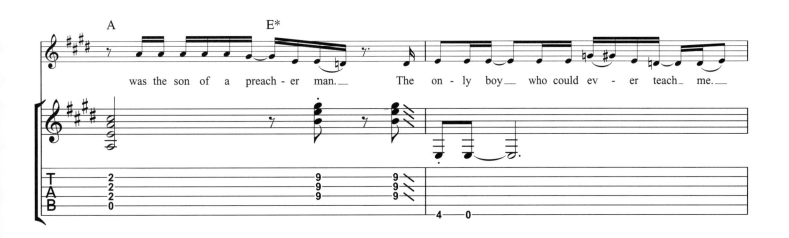

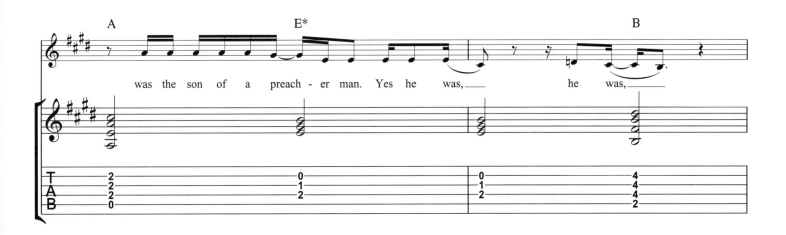

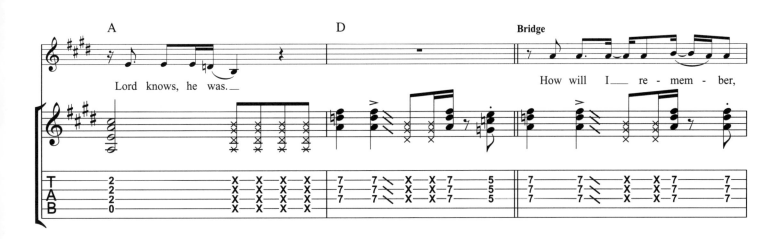

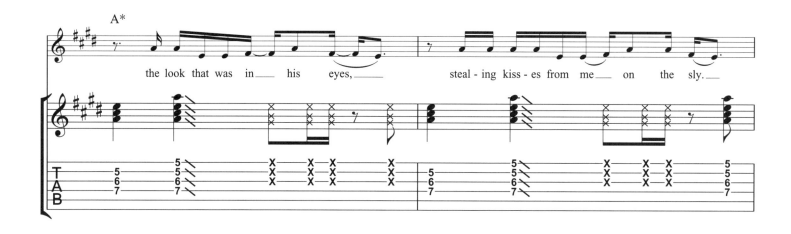

the look that was in his eyes, steal - ing kiss - es from me on the sly.

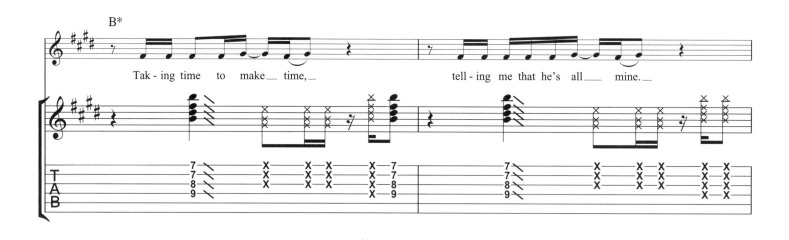

Tak - ing time to make time, tell - ing me that he's all mine.

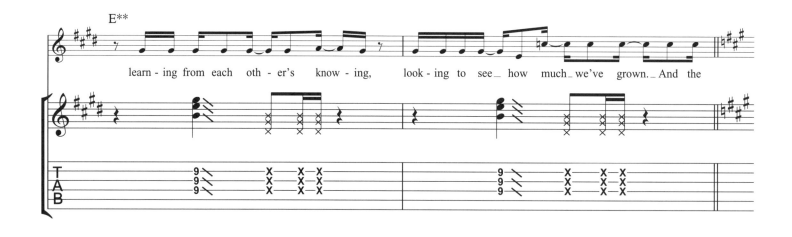

learn - ing from each oth - er's know - ing, look - ing to see how much we've grown. And the

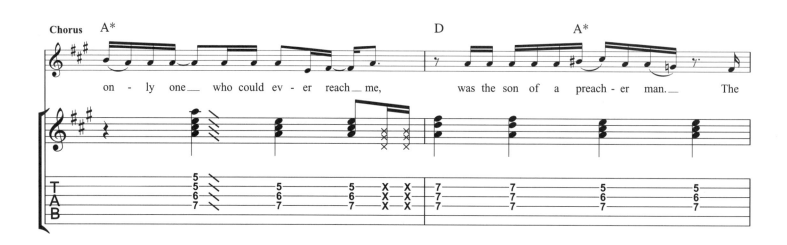

on - ly one who could ev - er reach me, was the son of a preach - er man. The

MONTE CARLO NIGHTS

By Elliot Easton

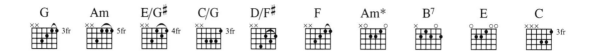

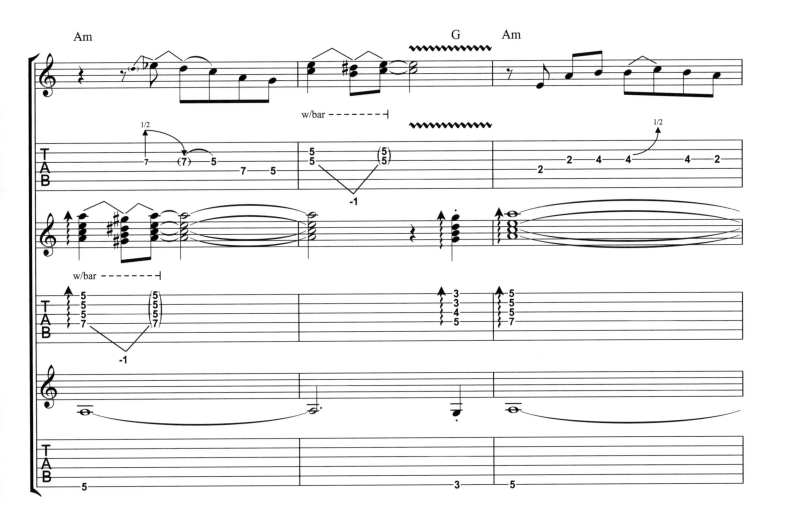

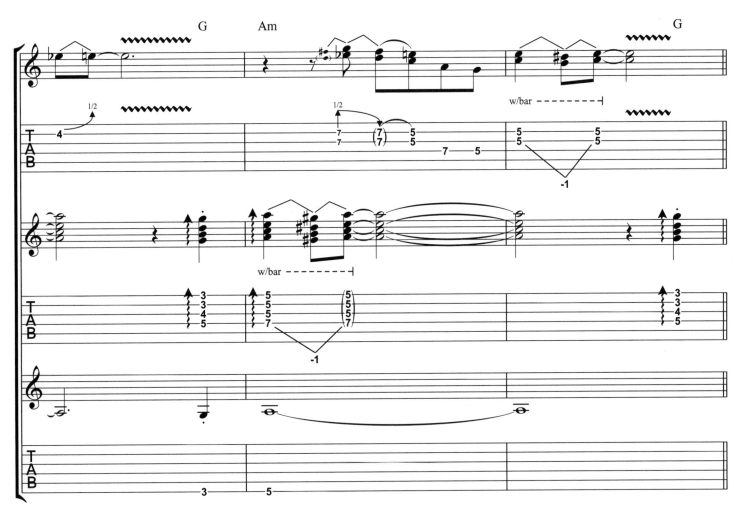

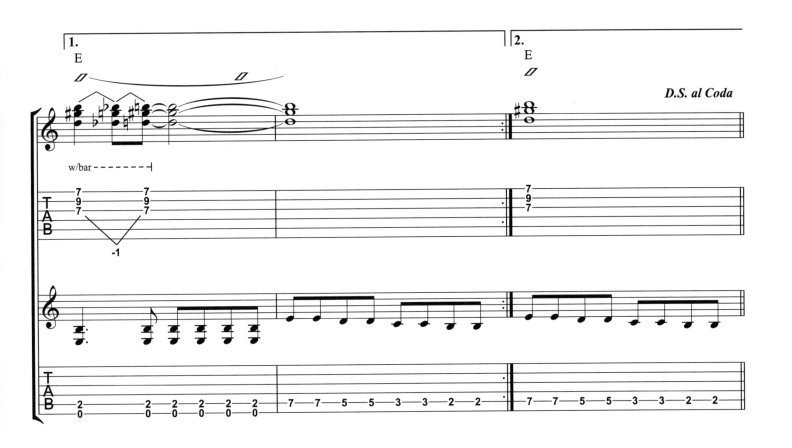

D.S. al Coda

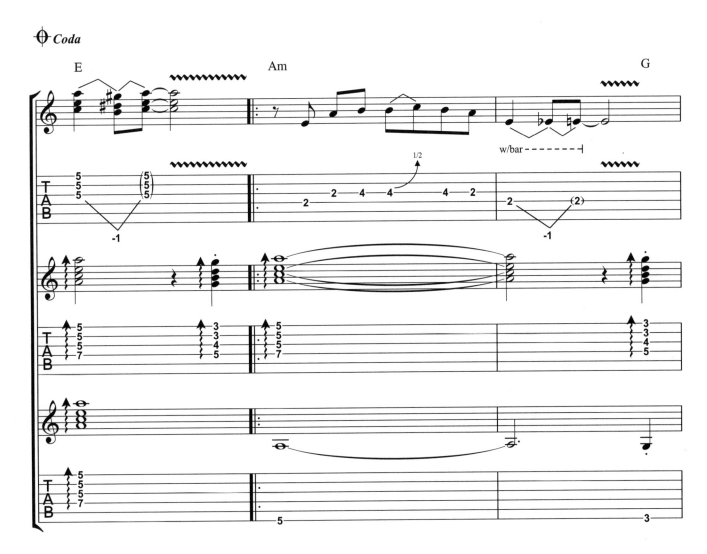

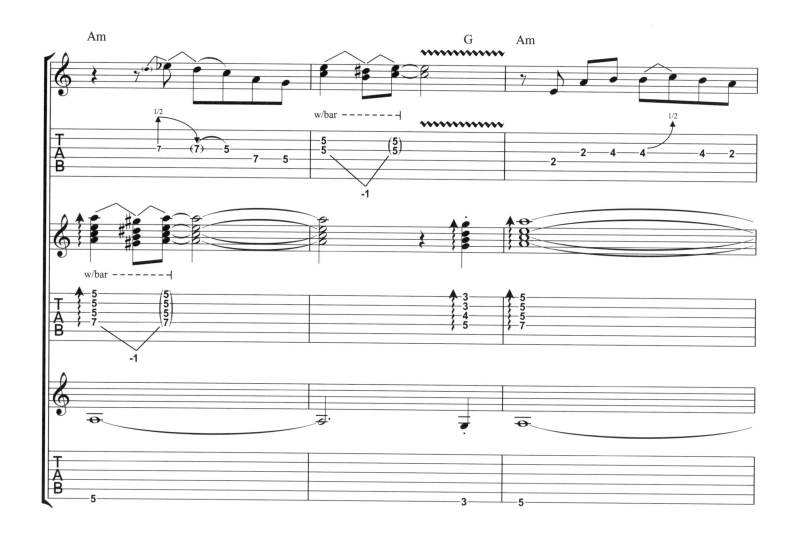

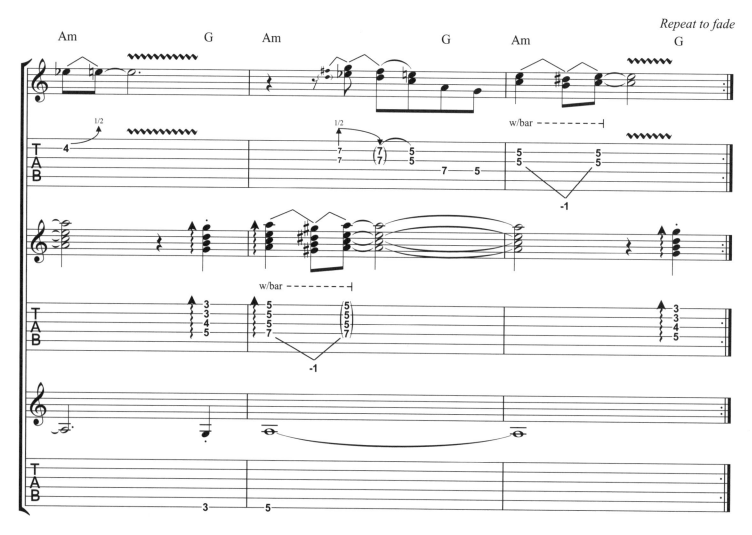

STUCK IN THE MIDDLE WITH YOU

Words & Music by Joe Egan & Gerry Rafferty

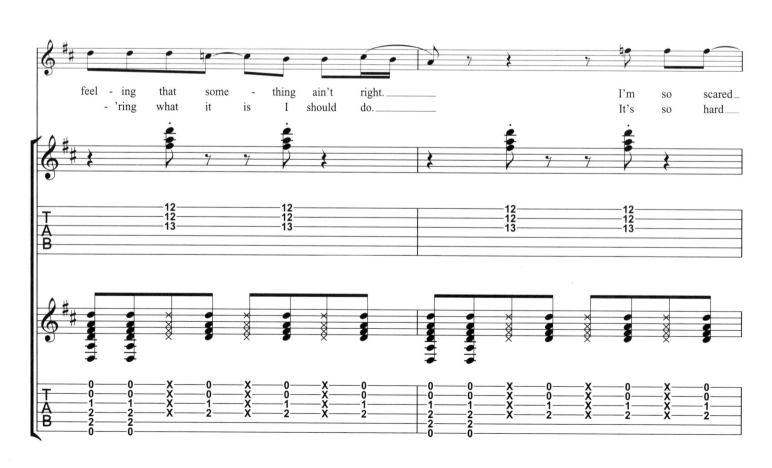

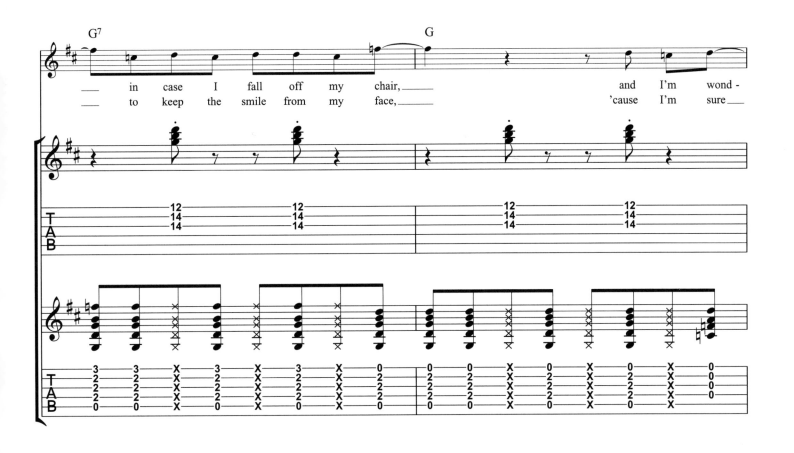

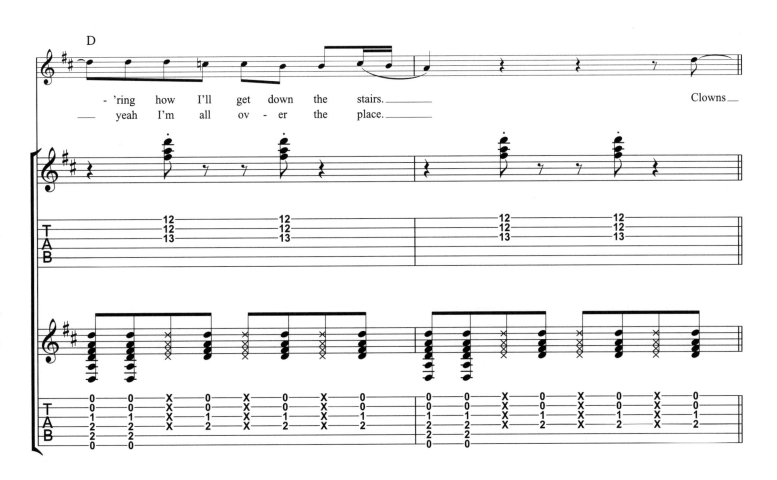

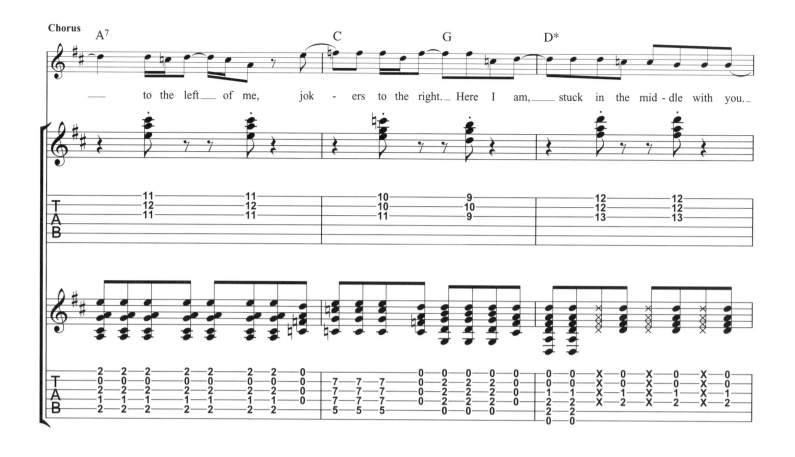

Chorus

to the left of me, jok - ers to the right. Here I am, stuck in the mid - dle with you.

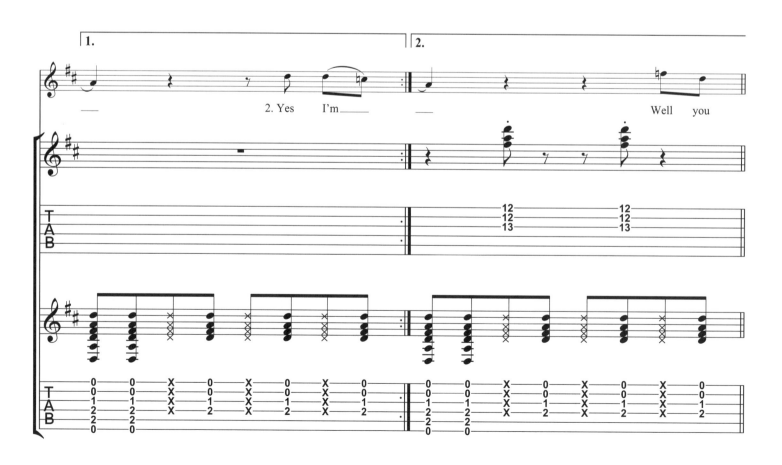

1.

2. Yes I'm

2.

Well you

that I can take an-y-more. _____ Clowns

-'ring how I'll get down the stairs. _____

...Fig. 1 ends

Chorus A⁷ C G

to the left _____ of me, jok - ers to the right. _____ Here I am,

81

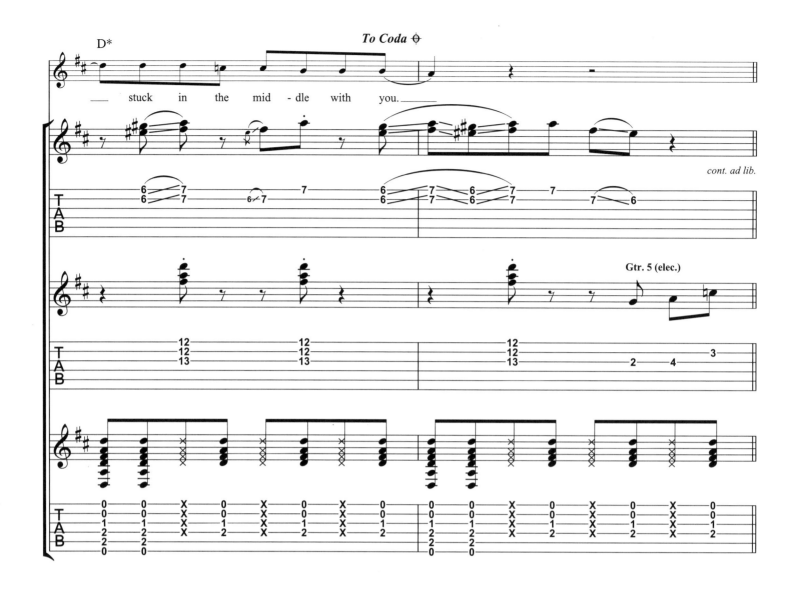

stuck in the mid - dle with you.

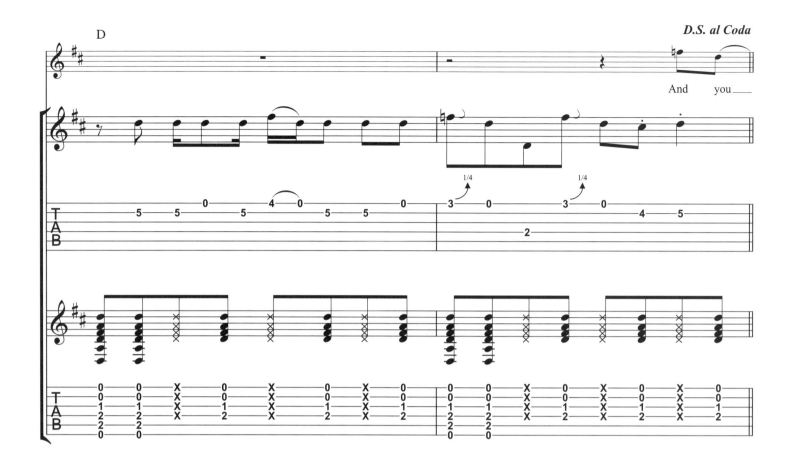

And you___

⊕ Coda

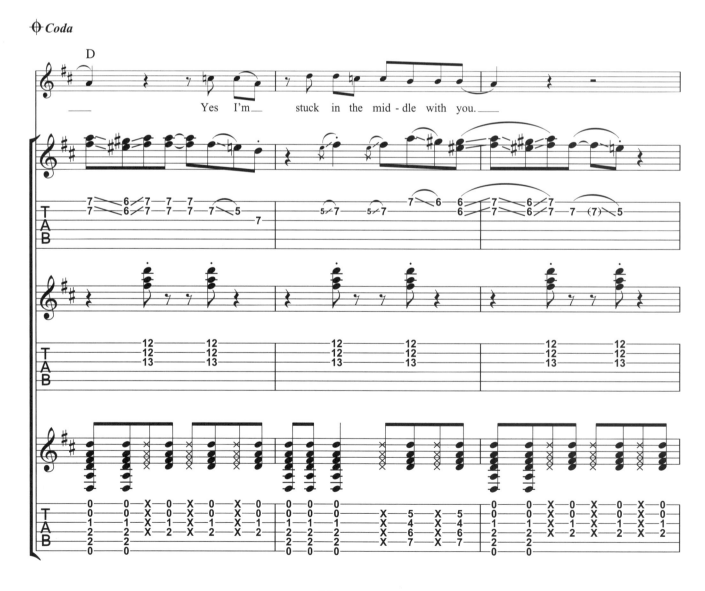

Yes I'm___ stuck in the mid - dle with you.___

stuck in the mid - dle with you. _____ Here I am, _____

_____ stuck in the mid -dle with you. _____

SURF RIDER

By Bob Bogle, Nole Edwards & Don Wilson

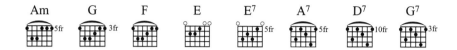

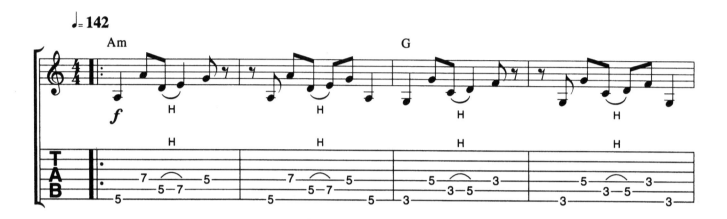

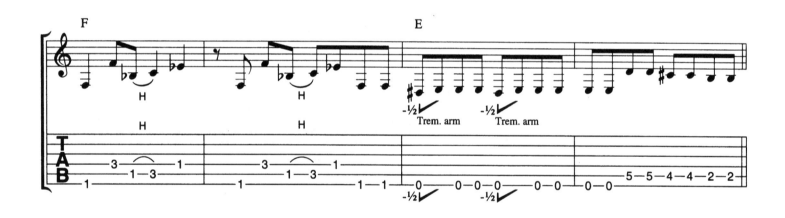

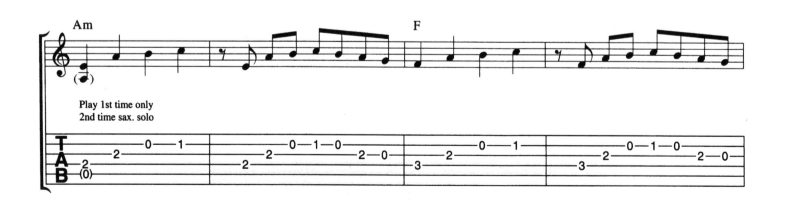

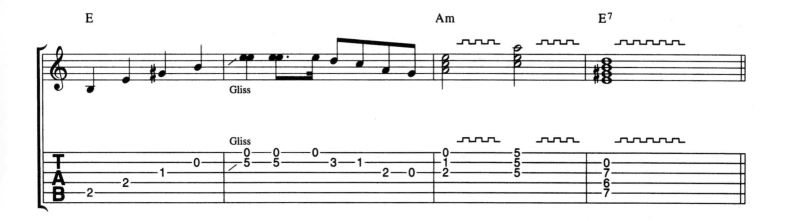

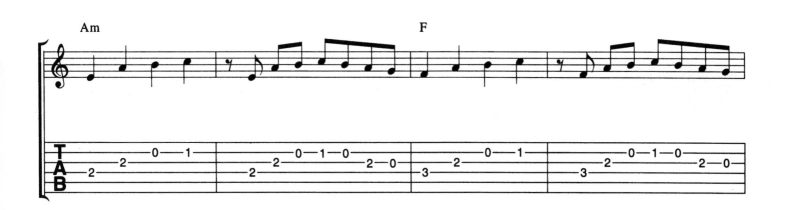

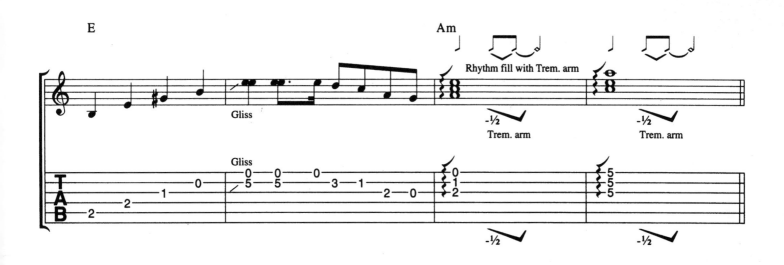

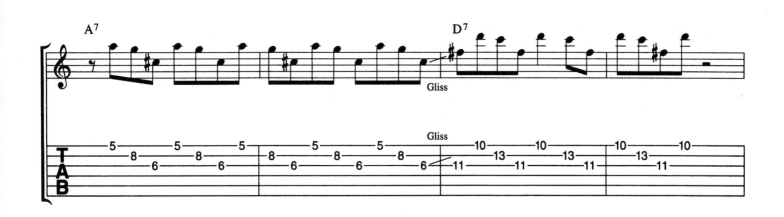

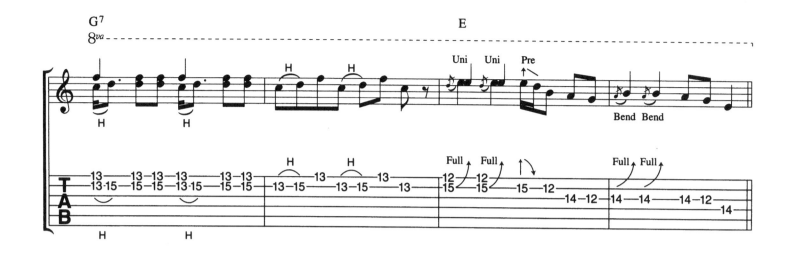

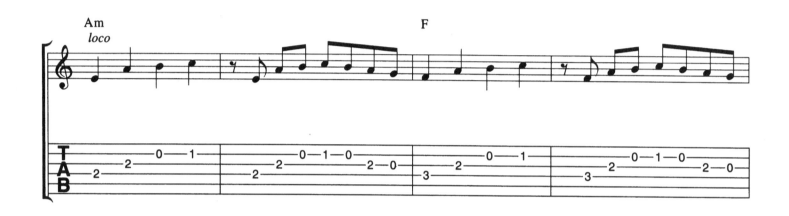

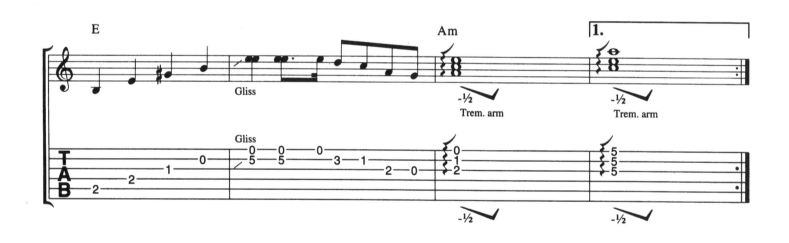

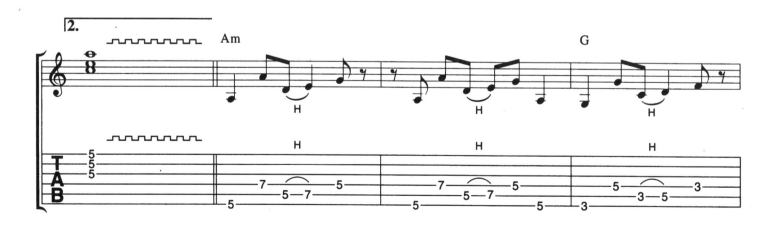

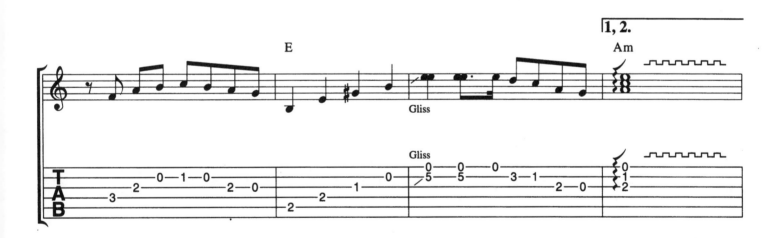

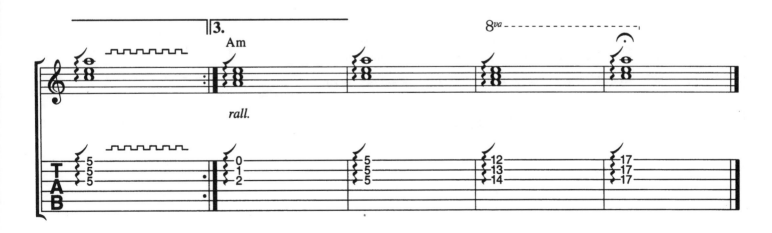

89

WOO HOO

Words & Music by George McGraw

Woo - hoo, woo - hoo hoo.

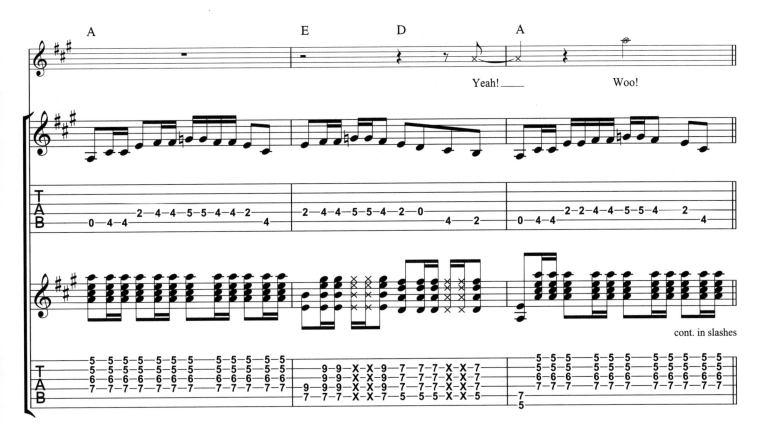

Yeah!___ Woo!

cont. in slashes

Chorus

Gtr. 2 _cont. sim._

Woo - hoo, woo - hoo - hoo. Woo - hoo, woo - hoo - hoo. Woo - hoo, woo - hoo - hoo.

Woo - hoo, woo - hoo - hoo. Woo - hoo, woo - hoo Woo - hoo, woo - hoo - hoo.

Bridge

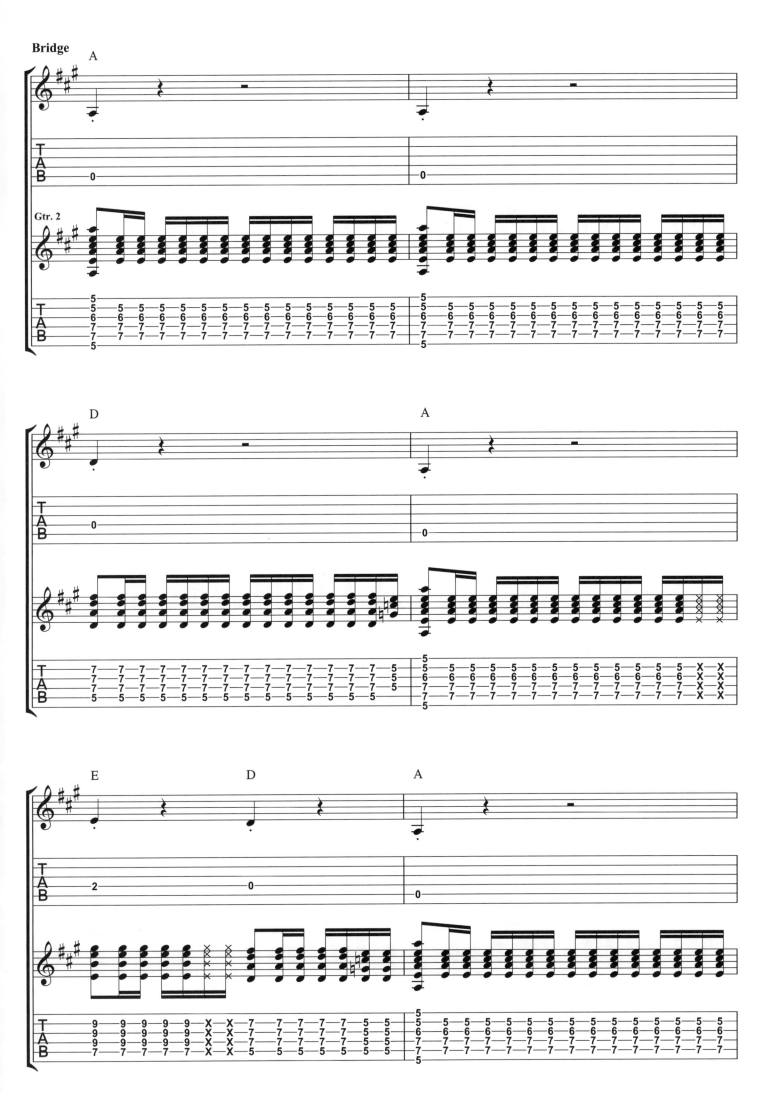

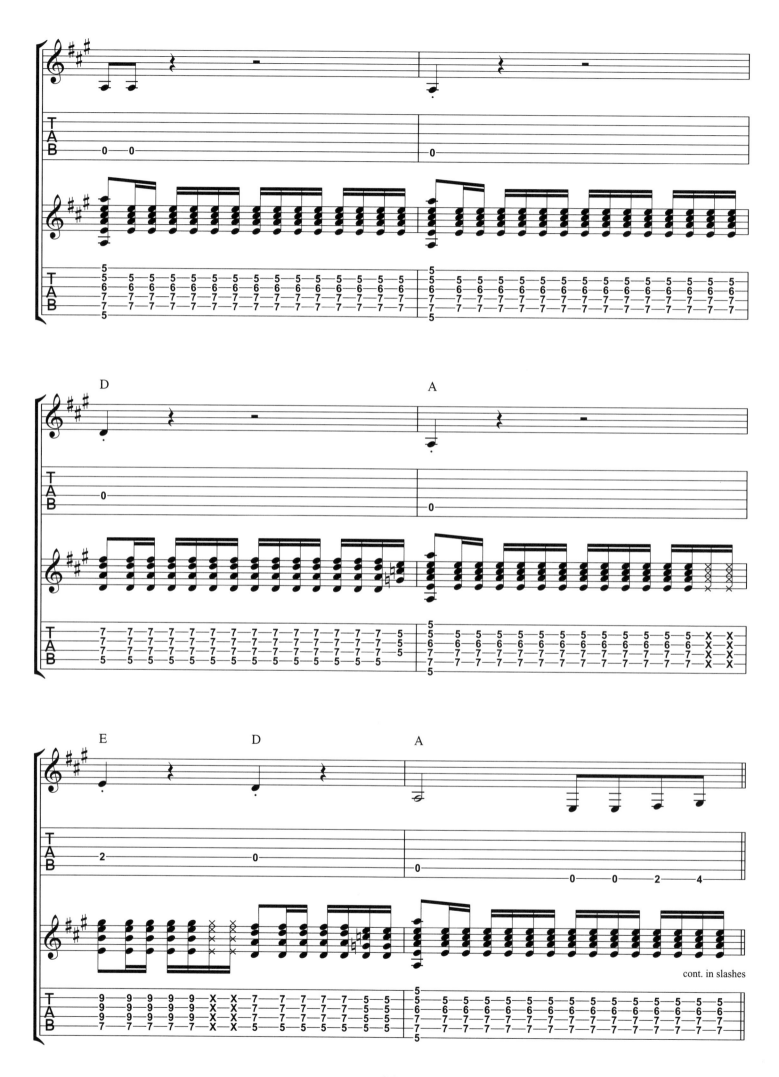

94

GUITAR TABLATURE EXPLAINED

Guitar music can be notated in three different ways: on a musical stave, in tablature, and in rhythm slashes.

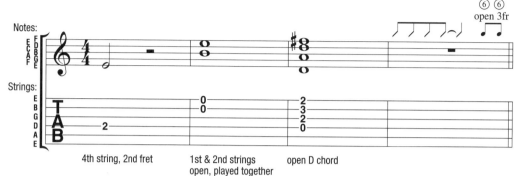

RHYTHM SLASHES are written above the stave. Strum chords in the rhythm indicated. Round noteheads indicate single notes.

THE MUSICAL STAVE shows pitches and rhythms and is divided by lines into bars. Pitches are named after the first seven letters of the alphabet.

TABLATURE graphically represents the guitar fingerboard. Each horizontal line represents a string, and each number represents a fret.

4th string, 2nd fret

1st & 2nd strings open, played together

open D chord

DEFINITIONS FOR SPECIAL GUITAR NOTATION

SEMI-TONE BEND: Strike the note and bend up a semi-tone (1/2 step).

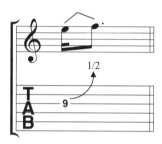

WHOLE-TONE BEND: Strike the note and bend up a whole-tone (whole step).

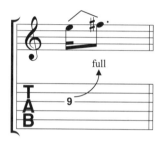

GRACE NOTE BEND: Strike the note and bend as indicated. Play the first note as quickly as possible.

QUARTER-TONE BEND: Strike the note and bend up a 1/4 step.

BEND & RELEASE: Strike the note and bend up as indicated, then release back to the original note.

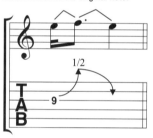

COMPOUND BEND & RELEASE: Strike the note and bend up and down in the rhythm indicated.

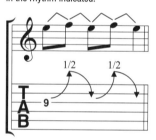

PRE-BEND: Bend the note as indicated, then strike it.

PRE-BEND & RELEASE: Bend the note as indicated. Strike it and release the note back to the original pitch.

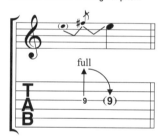

HAMMER-ON: Strike the first note with one finger, then sound the second note (on the same string) with another finger by fretting it without picking.

PULL-OFF: Place both fingers on the notes to be sounded, strike the first note and without picking, pull the finger off to sound the second note.

LEGATO SLIDE (GLISS): Strike the first note and then slide the same fret-hand finger up or down to the second note. The second note is not struck.

MUFFLED STRINGS: A percussive sound is produced by laying the fret hand across the string(s) without depressing, and striking them with the pick hand.

NATURAL HARMONIC: Strike the note while the fret-hand lightly touches the string directly over the fret indicated.

PICK SCRAPE: The edge of the pick is rubbed down (or up) the string, producing a scratchy sound.

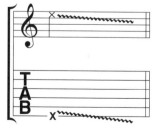

PALM MUTING: The note is partially muted by the pick hand lightly touching the string(s) just before the bridge.

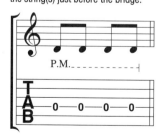

SHIFT SLIDE (GLISS & RESTRIKE): Same as legato slide, except the second note is struck.

NOTE: The speed of any bend is indicated by the music notation and tempo.